Bal
E4

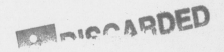

RAW MATERIAL

RAW MATERIAL

BY

DOROTHY CANFIELD

NEW YORK

HARCOURT, BRACE AND COMPANY

COPYRIGHT, 1923, BY
HARCOURT, BRACE AND COMPANY, INC.

PRINTED IN THE U. S. A. BY
The Quinn & Boden Company
BOOK MANUFACTURERS
RAHWAY   NEW JERSEY

CONTENTS

RAW MATERIAL

RAW MATERIAL

I DON'T know who is responsible for this rather odd book, but I lay it to the earlier generations of my family. My clergyman grandfather always said that he never enjoyed any sermons so much as the ones he preached to himself sitting under another clergyman's pulpit. When the text was given out, his mind seized on it with a vivid fresh interest and, running rapidly away from the intrusive sound of the other preacher's voice, wove a tissue of clear, strong, and fascinatingly interesting reasonings and exhortations. Grandfather used to say that such sermons preached to himself were in the nature of things much better than any he could ever deliver in church. "I don't have to keep a wary eye out for stupid old Mrs. Ellsworth, who never understands anything light or fanciful; I don't have to remember to thunder occasionally at stolid Mr. Peters to wake him up. I don't have to remember to keep my voice raised so that deaf old Senator Peaseley can hear me. I am not obliged to hold the wandering attention of their muddled heads by a series of foolish little rhetorical tricks or by a prodigious effort of my personality. I can just make my sermon what it ought to be."

My father, who did a great deal of public speaking, though not in pulpits, took up this habit in his turn. When a speaker began an address, he always fell into a trance-like condition, his eyes fixed steadily on the other orator, apparently giving him the most profound attention, but in reality making in his mind, on the theme suggested by the audible speaker, a fluent, impassioned address of his own. He used to say that he came to himself after one of these auto-addresses infinitely exhilarated and refreshed by the experience of having been speaking to an audience which instantly caught his every point, and which, although entirely sympathetic, was stimulatingly quick to find the weak spots in his argument and eager to keep him up to his best. Afterwards he dreaded an ordinary audience with its limping comprehension, its wandering attention, its ill-timed laughter and applause.

After I began to read for myself I found the same habit of mind familiar to many authors. The Stevensons walked up and down the porch at Saranac, talking at the tops of their voices, on fire with enthusiasm for their first conception of "The Wrecker." There never was, there never could be

(so they found out afterwards) a story half so fine
as that tale seemed to them in those glorious moments when they saw it as they would have liked to
make it. I nodded my head understandingly over
this episode. Yes, that was what, in their plain way,
my grandfather and father had done. I recognized
the process. It was evidently a universal one. And
when in "Cousine Bette" I encountered Wencelas
Steinbock, I recognized him from afar. "To muse,
to dream, to conceive of fine works, is a delightful
occupation. The work then floats in all the grace of
infancy, in the mad joy of conception, with the
fragrant beauty of a flower, and the aromatic juice
of a fruit enjoyed in anticipation."

And upon my own arrival in adult life it seemed
quite the expected and natural thing to find my own
fancy constantly occupied in this way. The stories
I told myself were infinitely superior to anything I
ever got down on paper. Just as my father had been
the ideal audience for himself, so I was my own best
reader, a reader who needed no long explanations,
who caught the idea at once, who brought to the tale
all the experience which made it intelligible. Two
words with the grocer's boy, delivering soap and
canned salmon at the back door, and I was off,
author and reader galloping along side by side, on a

story which made not only my own written tales, but
other people's as well, seem clumsy, obvious, and
wordy. A look on an old cousin's face was to me—
like a text to my grandfather—a springboard from
which author and reader plunged simultaneously
into the sea of human relationships, sensing in
human life significances pitiful, exalted, profound,
beyond anything that can be drawn out with the
loose-meshed net of words. Did I sit idling in a
railway station, my great-uncle, who died before
I was born, stood there beside me, expounding his
life to me with a precision, a daring abandon, a zest-
ful ardor which would wither and fade if it were
transferred to the pages of a book.

At first I thought this habit of mind entirely universal—as it is certainly the most natural one possible; but in the course of much random talk about
things in general, I have occasionally come across
people whose eyes are too weak for the white bril-
liance of reality, who can only see life through the
printed page, which is a very opaque object. Such
people—and they are often cultivated, university-
bred—will say, quite as if they were uttering a tru-
ism: "Of course characters in books—well-written
books—are ever so much more interesting than men
and women in real life."

They perceive the fateful mixture of beast and angel in the human face only in a portrait gallery; for them the birds sing, the winds sigh, and human hearts cry out, only at a symphony concert; they depend on books to give them faintly, dully, dimly, at third-hand, what lies before them every day, bright-colored, throbbing, and alive. It is a mental attitude hard for me to understand but it does exist. I have seen them turn away from a stern and noble tragedy in the life of their washerwoman, to the cheap sentimentality of a poor novel, which guarantees (as a fake dentist promises to fill teeth without pain) to provide tears without emotion. I have seen women who might have been playing with a baby, laughing at his inimitable funniness, leave him to a nurse and go out to enliven their minds by the contemplation of custard-pies smeared over the human countenance.

We are so used to this phenomenon that it does not seem strange to us. But it is strange—strange and tragic. And I do not in the least believe that the tragedy is one of the inevitable ones. I think it is simply a bad habit which has grown up as the modern world has taken to reading.

Why did the habit ever start? Naturally enough. Because the new medium of cheap printing let loose

on the world the innate loquacity of writers, unre-
pressed by the limitations of the human voice.
Other people have not been able to hear themselves
think since Gutenberg enabled writers to drown out
the grave, silent, first-hand mental processes of
people blessed by nature with taciturnity. The
writer is not born (as is his boast) with more capacity than other people for seeing color and interest
and meaning in life; he is born merely with an ir-
repressible desire to tell everybody what he sees and
feels. We have been hypnotized by his formidable
capacity for speech into thinking that he is the only
human being on whom life makes an impression.
This is not so. He is merely so made that he cannot rest till he has told everybody who will listen to
him, the impression that life has made on him.
This is the queer mainspring of creative literature.
The writer cannot keep a shut mouth. To speak
out seems to be the only useful thing he can do in
life. And in its way it is a very useful occupation.
But there is no reason why other people who have
other useful things to do should miss the purity and
vividness of a first-hand impression of life which
they could enjoy without spoiling it, as an artist always does, by his instant anxiety about how much
of it he can carry off with him for his art, by his in-

stant mental fumbling with technical means, by his anguished mental questions: "What would be the best way to get that effect over in a book?" or "How could you convey that impression in a dialogue?"

It is a dog's life, believe me, this absurd, pretentious carrying about of your little literary yardstick and holding it up against the magnificent hugeness of the world. I cannot believe that it is necessary to have that yardstick in hand before seeing the hugeness which it can never measure. One proof that it is not necessary is the fact that artists enjoy the raw materials of arts which they do not practise, much more freely and light-heartedly than the raw material of their own. I love the materials from which painters make pictures and musicians make music vastly more than the materials from which novelists make novels, because I feel no responsibility about them, because I know that they do not mean for me a struggle, foredoomed to failure, to get them down on canvas or between the five lines of the musical staff.

Do I seem to be advocating a habit of mind which would put an end to the writing of novels altogether? Personally I do not believe that the foundations of the world would move by a hair if that end were brought about. But, as a matter of fact, I do not in the least think that novel-writing would be anything but immensely benefited by a reading public which had acquired its own eyesight and did not depend on the writer's. Such a body of creative-minded readers would lift the art of fiction up to levels we have none of us conceived. With such a public of trained, practised observers, fiction could cast off the encumbering paraphernalia of explanations and photographs which now weigh it down. There need be no fear for the future of fiction if every one takes to being his own novelist. For then readers will not look in novels for what is never there, reality itself. They will look for what is the only thing that ought to be there, the impression which reality has made on the writer, and they will have an impression of their own with which to compare that of the writer. This will free the author forever from attempting the impossible, bricks-without-straw undertaking of trying to get life itself between the covers of a book.

For never, never can fiction hope to attain myriads of effects which life effortlessly puts over wherever we look, if we will only see what is there. If we leave those inimitable natural effects of beauty, or fun, or tragedy, or farce entirely for the professional writer to see and enjoy and ponder on, we are show-

ing the same sort of passive, closed imaginations
which lead Persians to sit obesely at ease on cush-
ions, and watch professional dancers have all the
fun of dancing. The phrase which we traditionally
ascribe to them is this, "Why bother to dance yourselves, when you can hire somebody to do it much
better?" But that is our own unspoken phrase
about the raw material of art and its monopoly
by the professional artist. We Westerners dance,
ourselves, not because we have any notion that we
can dance better than the professionals, but because
we have discovered by experience that to dance gives
us a very different sort of pleasure from that given
by looking at professionals. We have also discovered that it does not at all prevent us from hiring
professionals and enjoying them as much as any
Persians.

It is for the active-minded people who enjoy doing
their own thinking as well as watching the author
do his, that I have put this volume together. When
life speaks to them, their hearts answer, as a friend
to a friend. They are my brothers and my sisters.
They practise the delight-giving art of being their
own authors. They know the familiar, exquisite interest of trying to arrange in coherence the raw
material which life constantly washes up to every

one in great flooding masses. And they do this for their own high pleasure, with no idea of profiting by it in the eyes of the world. They work to create order out of chaos with a single-hearted effort, impossible to poor authors, tortured by the aching need to get the results of their efforts into words intelligible to others.

Being useful in other ways to the world, it is quite permissible for them to indulge in what was pernicious self-indulgence for an artist like Wencelas Steinbock. They are good children who, having nourished themselves on the substantial food of useful work, may eat candy without risking indigestion. The artist's work is the fatiguing attempt to transform the wonder of life into art! Those other disinterested observers of life, those wise, deeply pondering, far-seeing men and women, driven by their own need to make something understandable out of our tangled life, struggle, just as the artist does, to piece together what they see into intelligible order. But they do this in their own hearts, for their own satisfaction. How singularly free-handed and open-hearted and generous their attitude seems, compared to the artist's frugal, not to say penurious, not to say avaricious, anxiety to utilize every scrap of his life as raw material for his art.

Such people have, as the reward for their disinterested attitude of mind, all the pleasures of the creative artist's life and none of its terrible pains. All the pleasure, that is, except the dubious one of seeing themselves in print. This is—for me at least —a pleasure deeply colored with humiliation. The stuff which I manage to get into a printed book is so tragically dry and lifeless compared to the vibrating, ordered, succulent life which goes on inside my head before I put pen to paper! For my part, I envy the clever, happy people who are content to let it stay in their heads, and never try to decant it into a book, only to find that the bouquet and aroma are all gone. I quite sympathize with them when they are impatient with the verbose literal-minded garrulity with which most writers of fiction spread out clumsily over two pages that which takes but a flash to think or to feel. They think, and quite rightly, that what is slowly written out in the inaccurate, halting system we call language, bears little relation to the arrow-swift movements of the thinking mind and feeling heart.

That which is written down in an attempt to make it intelligible to everybody is a rude approximation like that of ready-made clothing, manufactured to fit every one somewhat and no one exactly. That which springs into being in the brain at a contact with life, exactly fits the comprehension, background, and experience of the person who owns the brain. There are no waste motions, no paragraphs to skip, no compressions too bare, no descriptions too wordy, none of those sore, never-solved problems of the writer who addresses unknown readers, "How much can I leave out? How far can I suggest and not state? How far can I trust the reader's attention not to flag, his intelligence to understand at a hint, rather than at a statement? What experience of life can I presuppose him to have had?"

When you are your own author, you know all about your reader, and need never think of his limitations. He is faithful to you, flies lightly when you rise into the air, plods steadily beside you at your own pace as you slowly work your way into unfamiliar country, flashes back into the past and selects exactly what is needed from his experience, sinks with you into a golden haze of contemplation over some surprising or puzzling phenomenon, is in no nagging hurry to "get on with the story." After some experience of such a marriage of author and reader, don't you find it hard to put up with the fumbling guesswork of a printed book?

And yet here I have written another book? No, this is not a written book in the usual sense. It is a book where nearly everything is left for the reader to do. I have only set down in it, just as if I were noting them down for my own use, a score of instances out of human life, which have long served me as pegs on which to hang the meditations of many different moods.

Note well that I have not set down those meditations . . . or at most—for the flesh is weak!—only here and there a trace of them. But if I have occasionally back-slid from the strait neutral path of sacred Objectivity, at least let me here and now warn you to ignore whatever moralizings of mine have escaped excision. Pay no attention to them, if you run across one or two. I know for a certainty that my musings about the men and women who were the originals of these portraits would not serve you as they do me. I know you can make for yourselves infinitely better ones. I know that what you will do for yourselves will be like the living lacework of many-colored sea-weed floating free and quivering in quiet sunlit pools; and that what I could get down in a book would be a poor little faded collection of stiff dead tendrils, pasted on blotting paper.

In this unrelated, unorganized bundle of facts,
I give you just the sort of thing from which a
novelist makes principal or secondary characters, or
episodes in a novel. I offer them to you for the
novels you are writing inside your own heads, before I have spoiled them by the additions, cuttings,
stretchings, or twistings necessary to make them fit
into the fabric of a book. I give them to you,
rounded and whole, just as they happened, without
filing and smoothing truth down to the limits of possibility as all fiction-writers are forced to do. I
spare you all the long-winded conventional devices,
descriptions, transitions, exposition, eloquent passages and the like, by which writers try to divert
the minds of their readers from the inherent im-
probability of their stories, devices which, to the
suspicious mind, resemble the patter of thimblerig-
gers at a county fair. You know as well as I how
inherently improbable life is. Why pretend that it
is not? I have treated you just as though you were
that other self in me who is my best reader. I have
given you the fare I like best.

And I have faith to believe that you will enjoy
for once being able to move about in a book without
a clutter of explanations and sign-boards to show
you the road the author wishes you to take. I do

not wish you to take any road in particular, and rather hope you will try a good many different ones, as I do. I have only tried to loan you a little more to add to the raw material which life has brought you, out of which you are constructing your own attempt to understand.

I am only handing you from my shelves a few more curiosities to set among the oddities you have already collected, and which from time to time you take down as I do mine, turning them around in your hands, poring over them with a smile, or a somber gaze, or a puzzled look of surprise.

UNCLE GILES

THERE are few personalities which survive the
blurring, dimming results of being the subject of
family talk through several generations; but the
personality of my Great-Uncle Giles has suffered
no partial obliteration. It has come down to us
with outlines keen and sharply etched into the family
consciousness by the acid of exact recollection.

This is not at all because Uncle Giles ever dis-
graced the family or did any evil or wicked action.
Quite the contrary! Uncle Giles thought that he
was the only member of the entire tribe with any
fineness or distinction of feeling, with any fitness
for a higher sphere of activities than the grubby
middle-class world of his kinsmen. Yes, that is
what Uncle Giles thought, probably adding to himself that he often felt that he was a "gentleman
among canaille." To this day the family bristles
rise at the mention of any one who openly professes
to be a gentleman.

A gentleman should not be forced to the menial
task of earning his living. Uncle Giles was never
forced to the menial task of earning his living.

None of the coarsely materialistic forces in human life ever succeeded in forcing him to it, not even the combined and violent efforts of a good many able-bodied and energetic kinspeople. The tales of how Uncle Giles blandly outwitted their stub-fingered attacks on his liberty and succeeded to the end of a very long life in living without work are endless in number and infinite in variety; and for three generations now have wrought the members of our family to wrath and laughter. He was incredible. You can't imagine anything like him. Unless you have had him in your family too.

For many years Uncle Giles was "preparing for the ministry." These were the candid years when his people did not know him so well as later, and still believed that with a little more help Giles would be able to get on his feet. He was a great favorite in the Theological Seminary where he was a student for so long, a handsome well-set-up blond young man, with beautiful large blue eyes. I know just how he looked, for we have an expensive miniature of him that was painted at the time. He paid for that miniature with the money my great-grand-father pried out of a Vermont farm. It had been sent to pay for his board. You can't abandon a son just on the point of becoming a clergyman and being a credit to the entire family. Great-grandfather himself had no more money to send at that time, but his other sons, hard-working, energetic, successful men, clubbed together and made up the amount necessary to settle that board-bill. Uncle Giles thanked them and forwarded with his letter, to show them, in his own phrase, "that their bounty was not ill-advised," a beautifully bound, high-priced, little red morocco note-book in which he had written down the flattering things said of him by his professors and others—especially others. He underlined certain passages, thus: ". . . a very worthy young man, *most pleasing in society.*" "A model to all *in the decorum and grace of his manners.*"

His board bill had to be paid a good many times before Uncle Giles finally gave up preparing himself for the ministry. The summer vacations of this period he spent in visiting first one and then another member of the family, a first-rate ornament on the front porch and at the table, admired by the ladies of the neighborhood, a prime favorite on picnics and on the croquet ground. He always seemed to have dropped from a higher world into the rough middle-class existence of his kin, but his courtesy was so exquisite that he refrained from commenting on this in any way. Still you could see that he felt it. Especially if you were one of the well-to-do neighbors on whom the distinguished young theological student paid evening calls, you admired his quiet tact and his steady loyalty to his commonplace family.

The effect which his quiet tact and steady loyalty had on his commonplace family was so great that it has persisted undiminished to this day. Any one of us, to the remotest cousin, can spot an Uncle Giles as far as we can see him. We know all about him, and it is not on our front porches that he comes to display his tact and loyalty, and the decorum and grace of his manners. As for allowing the faintest trace of Uncle-Gilesism to color our own lives, there is not one of us who would not rush out to earn his living by breaking stone by the road-side rather than accept even the most genuinely voluntary loan. We are, as Uncle Giles felt, a very commonplace family, of the most ordinary Anglo-Saxon stock, with no illuminating vein of imaginative Irish or Scotch or Welsh blood; and I think it very likely that if we had not experienced Uncle Giles we would have been the stodgiest of the stodgy as far as social injustice is concerned. But our imaginations seem to have been torn open by Uncle Giles as by a charge of dynamite; and, having once understood what he meant, we hang to that comprehension with all our dull Anglo-Saxon tenacity. We have a deep, unfailing sympathy with any one who is trying to secure a better and fairer adjustment of burdens in human life, because we see in our plain dull way that what he is trying to do is to eliminate the Uncle Gileses from society and force them to work. And we are always uneasily trying to make sure that we are not in the bigger scheme, without realizing it, Uncle Gilesing it ourselves.

After a while Uncle Giles stopped preparing for the ministry and became an invalid. He bore this affliction with the unaffected manly courage which was always one of his marked characteristics. He never complained: he "bore up" in all circumstances; even on busy wash-days when there was no time to prepare one of the dainty little dishes which the delicacy of his taste enabled him so greatly to appreciate. Uncle Giles always said of the rude, vigorous, hearty, undiscriminating men of the family, that they could "eat anything." His accent in saying this was the wistful one of resigned envy of their health.

It has been a point of honor with us all, ever since, to be able to "eat anything." Any one, even a legitimate invalid, who is inclined to be fastidious and make it difficult for the others, feels a united family glare concentrating on him, which makes him, in a panic, reach out eagerly for the boiled pork and cabbage.

Uncle Giles's was a singular case, "one of those mysterious maladies which baffle even the wisest physicians," as he used to say himself. A good many ladies in those days had mysterious maladies which baffled even the wisest physicians, and they used to enjoy Uncle Giles above everything. No other man had such an understanding of their symptoms and such sympathy for their sufferings. The easy chair beside Uncle Giles's invalid couch was seldom vacant. Ladies going away after having left a vaseful of flowers for him, and a plateful of cake, and two or three jars of jelly, and some cold breasts of chicken, would say with shining, exalted countenances, "In spite of his terrible trials, what an inspiration our friend can be! An hour with that good man is like an hour on Pisgah."

They would, as like as not, make such a remark to the brave invalid's brother or cousin (or, in later years, nephew) who was earning the money to keep the household going. I am afraid we are no longer as a family very sure what or where Pisgah is, although we know it is in the Bible somewhere, but there is a fierce family tradition against fussing over your health which is as vivid this minute as on the day when the brother or cousin or nephew of Uncle Giles turned away with discourteous haste from the shining-faced lady and stamped rudely into another room. Doctors enter our homes for a broken leg or for a confinement, but seldom for anything else.

When the Civil War came on, and Uncle Giles was the only man in the family left at home, he rose splendidly to the occasion and devoted himself to the instruction of his kinswomen, ignorant of the technique of warfare. From his invalid couch he explained to them the strategy of the great battles in which their brothers and husbands and fathers were fighting; and when the letters from hospital came with news of the wounded, who but Uncle Giles was competent to understand and explain the symptoms reported. As a rule the women of his family were too frantically busy with their Martha-like concentration on the mere material problems of wartime life to give these lucid and intellectual discussions of strategy the attention and consideration they deserved. The war, however, though it seemed endless, lasted after all but four years. And when it was over, Uncle Giles was free to go back to discussions more congenial to his literary and esthetic tastes.

By this time he was past middle-age, "a butterfly broken on the wheel of life," as he said; it was of course out of the question to expect him to think of earning his own living. He had become a family tradition by that time, too, firmly embedded in the solidly set cement of family habits. The older generation always had taken care of him, the younger saw no way out, and with an unsurprised resignation bent their shoulders to carry on. So, before any other plans could be made, Uncle Giles had to be thought of. Vacations were taken seriatim not to leave Uncle Giles alone. In buying or building a house, care had to be taken to have a room suitable for Uncle Giles when it was your turn to entertain him. If the children had measles, one of the first things to do was to get Uncle Giles into some other home so that he would not be quarantined. That strange law of family life which ordains that the person most difficult to please is always, in the long run, the one to please whom most efforts are made, worked out in its usual complete detail. The dishes Uncle Giles liked were the only ones served (since other men could "eat anything"); the songs Uncle

Giles liked were the only ones sung; the houses were adjusted to him; the very color of the rugs and the pictures on the walls were selected to suit Uncle Giles's fine and exacting taste.

Looking back, through the perspective of a generation-and-a-half, I can see the exact point of safely acknowledged middle-age when Uncle Giles's health began cautiously to improve; but it must have been imperceptible to those around him, so gradual was the change. His kin grew used to each successive stage of his recovery before they realized it was there, and nobody seems to have been surprised to have Uncle Giles pass into a remarkably hale and vigorous old age.

"Invalids often are strong in their later years," he said of himself. "It is God's compensation for their earlier sufferings."

He passed into the full rewards of the most rewarded old age. It was a period of apotheosis for him, and a very lengthy one at that, for he lived to be well past eighty. In any gathering Uncle Giles, erect and handsome, specklessly attired, his smooth old face neatly shaved, with a quaint, gentle, old-world courtesy and protecting chivalry in his manner to ladies, was a conspicuous and much-admired figure. People brought their visitors to call on him, and to hear him tell in his vivid, animated way of old times in the country. His great specialty was the Civil War. At any gathering where veterans of the War were to be honored, Uncle Giles held every one breathless with his descriptions of Gettysburg and Chancellorsville; and when he spoke of Mobile Bay and Sherman's march, how his voice pealed, how his fine eyes lighted up! Strangers used to say to themselves that it was easy to see what an eloquent preacher he must have been when he was in the active ministry. The glum old men in worn blue coats used to gather in a knot in the farthest corner, and in low tones, not to interrupt his discourse, would chat to each other of crops, fishing, and politics.

Somewhere we have a scrapbook in which an ironic cousin of mine carefully pasted in all the newspaper articles that were written about Uncle Giles in his old age, and the many handsome obituary notices which appeared when he finally died. I can remember my father's getting it out occasionally, and reading the clippings to himself with a very grim expression on his face; but it always moved my light-hearted, fun-loving mother to peals of laughter. After all, she was related to Uncle Giles only by marriage and felt no responsibility for him.

The other day, in looking over some old legal papers, I came across a yellowed letter, folded and sealed (as was the habit before envelopes were common) with three handsome pale-blue seals on its back. The seals were made with the crested cameo ring which Uncle Giles always wore, bearing what he insisted was the "coat of arms" of our family. The handwriting of the letter was beautiful, formed with an amorous pride in every letter. It was from Uncle Giles to one of his uncles, my great-grandfather's brother. It had lain there lost for half a century or more, and of course I had never seen it before; but every word of it was familiar to me as I glanced it over. It began in a manner characteristic of Uncle Giles's polished courtesy, with inquiries after every member of his uncle's family, and a pleasant word for each one. He then detailed the state of his health, which, alas, left much to be desired, and seemed, so the doctors told him, to require urgently a summer in the mountains. Leaving this subject, he jumped to the local news of the town where he was then living, and told one or two amusing stories. In one of them I remember was this phrase, "I told her I might be poor, but that a gentleman of good birth did not recognize poverty as a member of the family." Through a neat transi-

tion after this he led up again to the subject of his
health and to the desirability of his passing some
months in the mountains, "in the pure air of God's
great hills." Then he entered upon a discreet,
pleasant, whimsical reference to the fact that only a
contribution from his uncle's purse could make this
possible. There never was anybody who could
beat Uncle Giles on ease and grace, and pleasant,
pungent humor when it came to asking for money.
The only person embarrassed in that situation was
the one of whom Uncle Giles was expecting the loan.

I read no more. With no conscious volition of
mine, my hand had scrunched the letter into a ball,
and my arm, without my bidding, had hurled the ball
into the heart of the fire.

But as I reflected on the subject afterwards, and
thought of the influence which Uncle Giles has always had on our family, it occurred to me that I
was wrong. Uncle Giles ought not to be forgotten.
I ought to have saved that letter to show to my
children.

"WHAT GOES UP . . ."

AMONG the many agreeably arranged European lives which were roughly interrupted by the war, I know of none more snugly and compactly comfortable than that of Octavie Moreau. Indeed, for some years there had been in the back of my mind a faint notion of something almost indiscreet in the admirably competent way in which 'Tavie arranged her life precisely to her taste. I don't mean that it was an easeful or elegant or self-indulgent life. She cared as little for dress as any other intellectual Frenchwoman, let herself get portly, did up her hair queerly, and the rigorously hearth-and-home matrons of Tourciennes pointed her out to their young daughters as a horrible example of what happens to the looks of a woman who acquires too much learning. As for ease and self-indulgence, 'Tavie's vigorous personality and powerful, disciplined brain, as well as the need to earn her living, kept her from laying on intellectual fat. But all that vigorous personality, that powerful brain, as well as all the money which she competently earned, seemed more and more to be concentrated on her own comfort and

on nothing else. Her excellent salary as professor
of science in the girls' Lycée was almost doubled by
what she made by private lessons, for she was an
inspired natural teacher, who can, as the saying
goes, teach anybody anything. In the thirty years
of her life in Tourciennes she has pulled innumerable despairing boys and girls through dreaded examinations in science and mathematics; and parents
pay well, the world over, for having their boys and
girls pulled through examinations. They respect
the woman who can do it, even if, as in Octavie's
case, their respect is tempered with considerable
disapprobation of eccentric dress, irreligious ideas,
immense skepticism, and cigarette-smoking. And
in this case the respect was heightened by Mlle.
Moreau's well-known ability to drive a hard bargain
and to see through any one's else attempt to do the
same. Octavie had plenty of everything, brains,
will-power and money; but as far as I could see, she
never did anything with this plenty, except to
feather her own nest. I mean this quite literally,
for 'Tavie had a nest, a pretty, red-roofed, gray-
walled, old villa, in the outskirts of Tourciennes,
which she had bought years before at a great bargain, and which was the center of her life. Her
younger sister, a weaker edition of Octavie, who

lived with her, and kept house for her, and revolved
about her, and adored her, and depended on her,
joined with her in this, as in everything else. Those
two women visibly existed for the purpose of bringing to perfection that house and the fine, walled
garden about it. Long before anybody else in our
circle in France thought of such a thing as having
a real bathroom with hot and cold water, 'Tavie had
one, tiled, and glazed, and gleaming. Octavie's library was the best one (in science and economic
history) in that part of France. Never were there
such perfectly laid and kept floors as 'Tavie's, nor
such a kitchen garden, nor closets so convenient and
ingeniously arranged, nor a kitchen of such perfection. All well-to-do kitchens in the north of France
are works of art, but 'Tavie's was several degrees
more shining and copper-kettled and red-tiled and
polished than any other, just as the food which was
prepared there was several degrees more succulent,
even than the superexcellent meals served elsewhere
in that affluent industrial city of the North. As I
finished one of 'Tavie's wonderful dinners, and
stepped with her into the ordered marvel of her
great garden, I remember one day having on the tip
of my tongue some half-baked remark about how
far the same amount of intelligence and energy

would have gone towards providing more decent homes for a few of the poor in her quarter—for the housing of the poor in Tourciennes was notorious for its wretchedness. But you may be sure I said nothing of the sort. Nobody ventured to make any such sanctimonious comment to caustic Octavie Moreau, fifty-four years old, weighty, powerful, utterly indifferent to other people's opinions, her fine mind at the perfection of its maturity, her well-tempered personality like a splendid tool at the service of her will, her heart preserved from care about other people's troubles by her biological conviction of the futility of trying to help any one not energetic enough to help himself. She was not unkind to people she happened to know personally, occasionally spilling over on the needy ones a little of her superabundant vigor, and some of the money she earned so easily. But in her heart she scorned people who were either materially or morally needy, as she scorned every one who was weak and ignorant and timorous, who was not strong enough to walk straight up to what he wanted and take it. She had always done that. Anybody who couldn't . . . !

Then the war began and well-planned lives became like grains of dust in a whirlwind. Tourciennes was at once taken by the Germans and held until the very last of the war, and for more than four years none of the rest of us had a word from 'Tavie and her sister. Beyond the trenches Tourciennes seemed more remote than the palest asteroid.

But after the armistice, what with letters and visits, we soon learned all about their life under the German occupation, in most ways like the lives of all our other friends in the North, the grinding round of petty and great vexations and extortions and oppressions, and slow, dirty starvation of body, mind, and soul which has been described so many times since Armistice Day—but with one notable exception. To Octavie life had brought something more than this.

Early in the third year of the war, the grimly enduring town was appalled by a decree, issued from German Headquarters. In reprisal for something said to have happened in far-away Alsace-Lorraine, forty of the leading women of Tourciennes were to be taken as hostages, conveyed to a prison-camp in the north of Germany, and left there indefinitely till the grievance (whatever it was) in Alsace-Lorraine had been adjusted to the satisfaction of the German government.

By the third year of the war, every one in Tourciennes knew very well what deportation to a German prison-camp meant: almost sure death, and certainly broken health for the most vigorous men. They had all at one time or another gone to the railway station to meet returned prisoners, ragged, demoralized groups of broken, tubercular skeletons, who had gone away from home elderly but powerful men, leaders in their professions. And these latest hostages were to be women, delicately reared, not in their first youth, many of them already half-ill after three years of war privations. In order to make the deepest possible impression on the public of the captive city the most respected and conspicuous women were chosen, prominent either for their husband's standing and wealth or for the place they had made for themselves, by their own intelligence and energy: the Directress of the Hospital, a well known teacher of music, the Mayor's wife, the daughter of a noted professor. Of course, our Octavie was among the number.

We knew some of the others, too, either by reputation or personally, and could imagine the heart-sick horror in which their families saw them make their few hasty preparations for departure. Here is a typical case. One of the names on the list was that of Mme. Orléanne, a woman of seventy. She

was then so weak from malassimilation of war-food
that she had not been out of doors for months! It
was nothing less than a death-sentence for her. Her
family did not even let her see the list. Her elder
daughter, married to a wealthy manufacturer, went
to the German officials and offered herself to be deported as a substitute, although she had two children, a girl of eight and a little boy of three! She
was accepted, and, death in her heart, set about
making up the tiny bundle of necessaries—all they
were allowed to carry. Her little girl was old
enough to take up the tradition of tragic stoicism
of her elders and listened with a blanched face to
the instructions of her desperate mother, who told
her that there was now nothing but dignity left to
Frenchwomen. When the German guard came to
tell Mme. Baudoin that the truck which was to carry
the hostages away to the railroad was waiting at the
door, little Elise, rigid and gray, kissed her mother
good-by silently, though after the truck had gone,
she fainted and lay unconscious for hours. But
Raoul, only a baby, screamed, and struck at the
German soldier, clung wildly to his mother with
hysteric strength, and after she had gone, broke
away from his aunt, rushed out of the street door,
shrieking, "Mother, Mother! don't go away from

Raoul!" and flung himself frantically upon his mother's skirts. She said to me, as she told me of this, "dying will be easy compared to that moment!" But without weakening she did the intolerable thing, the only thing there was to do, she reached down, tore the little boy's tense fingers from her dress, and climbed up into the truck. "As I looked away from Raoul I saw that tears were running down the cheeks of the German guard who stood at the back of the truck."

Ah, this human race we belong to!

Shuddering with the anguish of such scenes of separation, the hostages were locked for three days into cattle-cars, cold, windowless, jolting prisons, where they lived over and over those unbearable last moments with children, or sisters, or parents, or husbands, whom they never expected to see again. At the end of this ordeal, the wretched women, numb, half-starved, limping along in their disordered garments, raging inwardly, inflamed with indignant hatred for the soldiers who marshaled them, were brought together in their prison and left alone, save for two bored guards who sat at the door and stared at them.

The prison camp was an enormous one in the north of Germany, a dreary clutter of rough wooden buildings thrown down on a flat, sandy plain, entangled and surrounded by miles of barbed-wire fencing. The prison-room allotted to the forty women from Tourciennes was a high, bare loft, like a part of an ill-built, hastily constructed barn. Around three walls were tiers of bunks, filled with damp, moldy straw, a couple of dirty blankets on each. In the middle of the room was a smallish stove, rather tall and thin in shape, with one hole in the top, closed by a flat lid. An iron kettle stood on the stove. Windows were set in one wall of the room. Under the windows ran a long bench, and before it stood a long table made of a wide board. There was nothing else to be seen, except grease and caked filth on the rough, unpainted boards of the floor and walls. The last of the women staggered into the room; the door was shut, and they faced each other in the gray winter light which filtered in through the smeared panes of the windows.

All during the black nightmare of the journey, every one of them had been quivering with suppressed anguish. Absorbed each in her own grief and despair, they had lain on the thin layer of straw on the floor of the freight car, at the end of their strength, undone by the ignominy of their utter defenselessness before brute force. The marks of tears showed on their gray, unwashed faces, but they had no more tears to shed now. They leaned against the walls and the bunks, their knees shaking with exhaustion, and looked about them at the dreary, dirty desolation of the room which from now on was to be their world. The guards stared at them indifferently, seeing nothing of any interest in that group of prisoners more than in any other, especially as these were women no longer young, disheveled, wrinkled, unappetizing, with uncombed, gray hair, and grimy hands.

A little stir among them, and there was Octavie, our 'Tavie, on her feet, haggard with fatigue, dowdy, crumpled, battered, but powerful and magnetic. She was speaking to them, speaking with the authority of her long years of directing others, with the weight and assurance of her puissant personality.

I can tell you almost exactly what she said, for the woman who were there and who told me about it afterwards, had apparently not forgotten a word! She began by saying clearly and energetically, like an older sister, "Come, come, we are all Frenchwomen, and so we have courage; and we all have brains. People with brains and courage have noth-

ing to fear anywhere, *if they'll use them.* Now let's
get to work and use ours, all for one and one for
all!"

Her bold, strong voice, her dauntless look, her
masterful gesture, brought them out of their lassi-
tude, brought them from all sides and corners of the
room, where they had abandoned themselves,
brought them in a compact group close about her.
She went on, her steady eyes going from one to the
other, "I think I know what is the first thing to do;
to take a solemn vow to stick by each other loyally.
You know it is said that women always quarrel
among themselves, and that all French people do.
We are in a desperate plight. If we quarrel ever,
at all: if we are divided, we are undone. We're of
all sorts, Catholics, free-thinkers, aristocrats, radicals, housekeepers, business-women, and we don't
know each other very well. But we are all women,
civilized women, Frenchwomen, sisters! Nobody
can help us but ourselves. But if we give
all we have, they can never conquer us!"

She stopped and looked at them deeply, her
strong, ugly face, white with intensity. "A vow, my
friends, a vow from every one of us, by what she
holds most sacred, that she will summon all her
strength to give of her very best for the common

good. In the name of our love for those we have
left—" her voice broke, and she could not go on.
She lifted her hand silently and held it up, her eyes
fixed on them. The other hands went up, the drawn
faces steadied, the quivering hearts, centered each
on its own suffering, calmed by taking thought for
others. The very air in the barrack-room seemed
less stifling. The two German guards looked on,
astonished by the incomprehensible ceremony.
These scattered, half-dead women, flung into the
room like cattle, who had not seemed to know each
other, all at once to be one unit!

Octavie drew a long breath. Then, homely, familiar, coherent as though she were giving a pre-
liminary explanation to a class at the beginning of
a school-year, "Now let us understand clearly what
is happening to us, so that we can defend ourselves
against it. What is it that is being done to us? An
attempt is being made to break us down, physically
and morally. But these people around us here are
not the ones who wish this; they are not as intelligent as we; and they haven't half the personal
incentive to accomplish it, that we have to prevent
it. We have a thousand resources of ingenuity that
they can't touch at all.

"We must begin by economizing every atom possible of our strength, moral and physical. And we can start on that right now by not wasting any more strength hating our guards as we have all been hating the Germans who have had to touch us, so far. We can think of them as demons and infernal forces of evil and make them into horrors that will shadow our every thought. Or we can look straight at them to see what they are, and disregard them, just leave them out of our moral lives, when we see that they are ordinary men, for the most part coarse and common men, and now forced to be abnormal, forced by others into a situation that develops every germ of brutality in them."

At this, young Mme. Baudoin spoke out and told of the German guard who had wept when her little boy was dragged away; and, "I'd rather be in my shoes than his," cried Octavie vigorously.

"So then we sweep them out of our world," she went on, "and that leaves the decks cleared for real action. I should say," she went on with a change of manner, including in one wide humorous glance her own dirty hands, the tangled hair of the others, and the grease and grime of the room, "that the next thing is to organize ourselves to get clean! It's plain only a few of us can do it at a time; let's draw lots to see who begins, and the others can lie down while they wait. Is there anybody here who speaks German enough to ask for soap and water? I see the broom here at hand." A good many of the women proved to have studied German at school, and three of them spoke it. But this did not carry them far. The guards laughed at the idea of soap— nobody in Germany had had soap for months— prisoners were not given such luxuries as towels, and as for water, the tap was down the hall, and the pail was there, and they could carry it for them- selves. Besides there was water in the kettle on the stove.

There and then they began their campaign. Lots were drawn, a certain number of tired women col- lapsed into the bunks to wait, while Octavie organ- ized the others into squads, some to carry water; some to arrange a bathing-place in a corner of the room by hanging up their cloaks on strings stretched from nails; some to sweep out the worst of the dusty litter on the floor.

There was order and purpose in the air. The first woman who emerged from behind the curtain of cloaks, bathed, fresh linen next her clean skin (for they had been allowed to bring one change of linen in their little packages), her hair in order, was like a being from another world, the world they had left. Self-respect came back to the others, as they looked at her.

By night every woman was clean, had arranged her small belongings in her own bunk, and had washed out and hung up the body-linen which she had worn on the trip. One empty bunk had been set aside as the pharmacy, and all their little stock of medicine gathered there; another was the library, where a half-dozen books stood side by side; and a third was the storeroom for miscellaneous goods, the extra bars of soap they had brought from home, a little chocolate, thread, needles, scissors, and the like, communistically put together to be used for whatever proved to be the greatest need. They had taken stock of their material resources and agreed to share them. They had eaten what they could of the coarse, unpalatable food brought to them in the evening, and now sat on the long bench and on the floor, trying to plan out the struggle before them, the struggle to construct an endurable life out of the materials at hand. Octavie was saying, "Everything in order! That is the French way to go at things; classify them and take them up one by one. What are we? Bodies and minds; both equally in danger. Now, the body first. We must have exercise out of doors, more than we're used to at home, if we are to digest this awful food. They say we're to be allowed out an hour a day, but that is not enough. We must open the windows once an hour and do something active in here. Any volunteers to show us gymnastic exercises? Anybody who remembers them from school days? I don't know one."

Yes, there were several, and one whose sister was a woman doctor using curative gymnastics. The meeting voted to make them an athletic committee, to organize such activities.

"Now, our digestions. You know how all prisoners in Germany have always come home with ruined digestions. Is there anything we can do here? Is there anybody here experienced in cooking who could guess at the raw materials in that fearful mess we've just finished, and does she think it might be cooked more intelligently so that it would be better? It stands to reason that the prison cooks would naturally be incompetent, and indifferent to their results. Could we do better ourselves? It also stands to reason that we'd be allowed to, because it would mean less work for the prison kitchens." A group of housewives was appointed to consider this, next day.

"Now, as to cleanliness. Any suggestions about how to get along with no soap? We don't dare use soap on the floor, we have so little, but heaven knows it needs it!" All the practical housekeepers spoke at once now, crying out upon her lack of ingenuity in not thinking of sand. That sandy path outside the barracks, that would do excellently well as an abrasive. With plenty of water and energy, sand and some bricks for rubbing, everything in the room could be cleaned. As they spoke, their faces brightened at the prospect of having cleanliness about them, and of being active once more.

"Anything more for the body?" asked Octavie. "If we keep it exercised and clean, and as well-fed as we can manage it, it ought to last us. Now for the mind. We're going to have hours and hours of leisure time such as we busy women never had before. It's the chance of our lives to go on with our education. Let's share each of us with the other, what we have in our minds. I'll begin. I have chemistry thoroughly, economic history fairly, and the general theory of physics. I'll give a course of lectures on those. Who can do something else?"

They were all appalled at this and protested that she was the only one who had any information to impart; but she scouted the idea and began a relentless person-to-person inquiry. The result was that a group of musicians were organized, under the guidance of the music teacher, to give lectures on the history of music, the lives and works of the composers, church music, ballads, songs, and operas. Three other women who had brought up great families were to dive deep into their memories and lecture to the others, as logically, coherently, and rationally as they could on proper care for children. A shy, thin, drab-colored woman was found to have been brought up in Indo-China, and was to lecture on the life and education of that country. The German-speaking ones were to give a course in German. Another, the daughter of a well-known professor of French literature, was to assemble and arrange what she knew, and be prepared to plan and lead literary discussions. Another, the distinguished founder and former head of the best hospital in Tourciennes, would lecture on the care of the sick— and so on. From one, from another, from them all, Octavie drew potential treasures of experience and information which lay almost visibly shimmering in a great heap before them—"Enough," she cried triumphantly, "to last us for years!"

"And now because we're not solemn Anglo-Saxons, but Frenchwomen, we must plan for some fun, if we're to keep themselves alive," she told them

firmly, and at their sad-hearted wincing from the
idea, she said, "Yes, we must. It's part of our de-
fensive campaign. Our task is to construct out of
our brains and wills a little fortress of civilization,
and to protect ourselves behind its walls against de-
moralization and barbarism! And you all know
that amusement is needed for civilization!" A majority agreed to this, a dramatic committee was appointed, and another one on games (Octavie suggested drawing checker-boards on the tables, playing with bits of paper for men, and starting a free-
for-all tournament); some one else thought of manu-
facturing balls and inventing games to be played
with them, and there were two packs of cards, in the
miscellaneous store. The musical group undertook
to provide a weekly concert.

One of the subjects which had been canvassed and
found no professor was the history of France; but
like all French people, they had been soundly and
carefully instructed in history and planned, by putting all their memories together, to reconstruct the
story of their nation. The meeting was trailing off
from serious, purposeful planning to a discursive attempt to get the list of French kings complete, when
one of the older women spoke to Octavie in a low
tone, the quality of which instantly made silence

about them. She said, "But Mlle. Moreau, we have souls too, souls hard beset."

Up to this moment Octavie had, as always, dominated the situation! Now she, who has not been inside a church since she was a child, and who considers herself thoroughly emancipated from what she calls, "all that theological nonsense," was brought up short before the need to make just such a whole-hearted concession to other people's ideas as she had urged on her comrades! She looked hard at the speaker. It was the foundress of the hospital, Mme. Rouart. From her eyes looked out a personality just as strong as Octavie's, and tinctured to the core with faith. Octavie's arrogant intellectualism humbled itself at the sight. She made a gesture of acquiescence and was silent. Mme. Rouart went on, "We're of all sorts of belief, but we can all pray."

Then, after an instant's pause, she said in a low, trembling voice, "Let us pray."

There was an interval of intense silence, during which, so Octavie told me afterwards, quite without any shade of irony, she "prayed as hard as any one . . . and after that I prayed every evening when the others did."

"How did *you* pray?" I asked her, incredulously.

Her definition of prayer was characteristic. "I

set every ounce of will power to calling up all my strength and endurance. It was wonderful how I felt it rise, when I called," she said gravely. She added that on that first evening after her silent plunge to the deep places of power in her soul, she put both arms around Mme. Rouart's neck and kissed her. "I loved her," she said simply, without attempting her usual skeptical, corrosive analysis of reasons.

Other kisses were exchanged, soberly, as the stiff, tired women stumbled to their feet to go to bed. They laid their exhausted bodies down heavily on the dirty blankets, but in their hearts which had seemed burned out to ashes with grief, indignation, and despair, there shone a living spark of purpose. Some time later, into the darkness came the voice of one of the younger women. "Oh, I've just remembered! That fourth son of Clovis was Charibert;" to which Octavie's voice answered exultantly, "Ah, they never can beat *us!*"

The life which went on after this seems as real to me as though I had lived it with them, because when I first saw them, they were fresh from it, and could speak of little else. Every day was thrust at them full of the noisome poison of prison life, idleness, indifference, despair, bitterness, hatred, per-

sonal degeneration; and every day they poured out
this poison resolutely and filled its place with intelligent occupation! Just to keep clean was a prodigious undertaking, which they attacked in squads,
turn by turn. With sand, water, and bricks for
rubbing, they kept the room immaculate, though it
took hours to do it. Even the blankets were washed
out after a fashion, one by one at intervals, by
women who had never before so much as washed out
a handkerchief. To prepare the food with the more
than inadequate utensils and poor materials and the
stove unsuited for cooking was a tremendous problem, but they all took turns at it, Octavie humbly
acting as scullery-maid when her turn for service
came; and the food, though poor, monotonous, and
coarse, was infinitely superior, being prepared with
brains and patience, to what was served all around
them to the apathetic, healthless mobs of Russian
and Polish women and men, sunk despairingly in
degradation and disease, "giving up and lying
down in their dirt," Octavie told me, "to die like
beasts."

The older and weaker women among the Tourciennes group, who could not holystone the floor and
carry water and wood, were set at the lighter tasks,
the endless mending which kept their garments

from becoming mere rags, peeling turnips, washing
dishes, "making the beds" as they called the process
of drying and airing the straw in the bunks.

Every day they went out in all weathers, and
exercised and played ball with their home-made,
straw-stuffed balls, and every evening they played
games, checkers, guessing games, capped rimes,
told stories and sang. They all "studied singing"
and sang in twos, trios, quartets, or the whole forty
in a chorus. They sang anything any one could remember, old folk-songs of which there are such an
infinite variety in French, ballads, church-chants,
songs from operas.

Octavie told me that one evening, when the false
news which was constantly served to them was spe-
cially bad, when they had been told that half the
French Army was taken prisoner, and the other
half in retreat south of Paris, they sang with the
tears running down their cheeks, but still sang, and
kept their hearts from breaking.

Every day there were "lessons." Octavie was the
only trained teacher among them, so that her courses
in general science and in economic history were the
most professional of the instructions given; but she
sedulously attended the "courses" given by the
others, putting her disciplined mind on the matter

they had to present, and by adroit questionings and summarizings, helped them to order it coherently and logically. Once a week they had dramatics, scenes out of Molière, or Labiche, or Shakespeare, or Courteline, farce, tragedy, drama, anything of which anybody had any recollection, with improvisations in the passages which nobody could remember. The German guards looked on astonished at the spirit and dash of the acting, and the laughter and applause from the bunks, where the audience was installed to leave the room clear for a stage. Mme. Baudoin told me that she had never begun to suck the marrow out of the meaty Molière comedies, as she did in the stifling days of midsummer when they were giving a series of his plays.

By midsummer they had learned that one of the younger married women had been pregnant when she left France, that a French child was to be born in that German prison. How they all yearned over the homesick young mother! How important old Mme. Rouart became with her medical and nurse's lore! What anxious consultations about the preparations of the layette, manufactured out of spare undergarments and a pair of precious linen sheets brought from home. They were supposed to have medical attention furnished in the prison, but they had seen too much of the brutal roughness of the overworked and indifferent army-surgeons of the camp, not to feel a horror at the thought of their attending delicate little Mme. Larçonneur. She begged them desperately not to call in a doctor, but themselves to help her through her black hours. They were terrified at the responsibility, and as her time drew near, with the ups and downs of those last days, they were almost as frightened and tremulous as she.

But the night when she called out in a strangled voice that she needed help, found them all organized, each one with her work planned: some who sprang from their beds to heat water; Mme. Rouart prepared as far as her poor substitute for a nurse's outfit would allow her; others ready to lift the shivering, groaning woman from her own bunk to the one which had been cleaned, sterilized with boiling water, and kept ready. The others, who could not help, lay in their beds, their hands clenched tightly in sympathy with the suffering of their comrade, shaken to the heart, as the old drama of human life opened solemnly there in that poor place.

When the baby came, his high-pitched cry was like a shout of triumph.

"All well," announced the nurse to the anxious

women, "a fine little boy. No! nobody must stir!
Perfect quiet for Mme. Larçonneur." She busied herself with the mother, while her two assistants oiled
the baby and wrapped him in flannel, gloating over
the perfections of his tiny finished body, and murmuring to the faces showing over the bunks, "Such
a beauty! Such a darling! His little hands!—
Oh, see how he fights us!"

The next morning they formed in line to worship
him as he lay sleeping beside his mother, and although the sight brought a fierce stab of misery to
all the mothers who had left their children behind,
the little boy brought into their lives an element of
tenderness and hopeful forward-looking which was
curative medicine for their sick, women's hearts.

For in spite of all Octavie's moral and physical
therapeutics, there were intolerable moments and
hours and days for all of them. Women, loving
women, used to a life-time of care for others, used
to the most united family life, left for months at a
time without the slightest news of those they had
left, could not, valiantly as they might try, master
the fury of longing and anxiety which sprang upon
them in the midst of the courageously planned life
which they led. They all came to recognize in others
the sudden whiteness, the trembling hands, the fixed,

unseeing eyes blinded by tears. As far as loving whole-hearted sympathy could ease human hearts, such moments of unendurable pain were tempered by a deep sense of the sharing by all of each one's sorrow.

And then, of course, there were other bad moments and days, meaner, pettier enemies to fight, when it took all of one's self-control to prevent explosions of irritability from overwrought nerves; quarrelsome bitterness, which comes from brooding on grievances; sudden captious hatred for other people's mannerisms, which, in all prison-camps, almost as much as physical suffering, embittered and poisoned prison-life for the high-strung, finely organized, twentieth century prisoners of the Great War. Forty women, with lowered physical health, with heightened nervous sensibility, used to fastidious privacy, now shut up together in one room, with no chance ever to escape each other, crowded each other morally almost as much as physically. Octavie told me there were days when she would have liked to slap them, weak, wavering, superstitious souls that they seemed to her, and turn her face to the wall in her bunk to concentrate on hating the human race. And one of the devout Catholics told me that she often longed so intensely for her old

atmosphere of belief and faith that she was almost ill.
But they adopted as their battle-cry, "All together
to defend our civilization!" and, clinging fiercely to
this resolve, they fought away from everything that
might have separated them and struggled out on
ground common to them all.

Then Winter was there again, endless, empty,
gray days. There was sickness in the camp, a terrible wave of influenza, carrying off hundreds all
around them. They redoubled their cleanliness,
boiled every drop of water, exercised, played,
mended, studied, cooked, sang, kept steadily on with
the ordered precision of their lives. But old Mme.
Rouart, the one they loved the most of all, who led
the silent prayer of every evening, fell ill, endured
silently a few bitter days of suffering, died, and was
borne out from among them to be buried in alien
soil. Three others were desperately ill, lay near to
death, and slowly recovered. Tragedy drew them
more closely together than ever, as they realized how
utterly they depended on each other, and after this
there were fewer struggles against black days of bad
temper. The little boy was seven months old now,
laughed and crowed, and played with his fingers.

Time seemed to stand still for them, as they fought
to protect their little shining taper of civilization,

feeding it from their hearts and minds. When they
went outdoors for the daily escape from their room
to the sandy, hard-trodden desert of the prison yard,
they seemed with their neat, threadbare, faded,
well-mended garments, with their gray, carefully
dressed hair, their pale faces, clean and quiet, with
brave eyes and smiling lips, like another order of
being from the shaggy, dirt-crusted, broken-down
Polish and Russian soldiers, whose corrals were on
each side of them, lying listlessly in the drizzling
mist or quarreling among themselves. They were
known by this time all over the camp, and the demoralized, desperate men watched the decent
Frenchwomen with that most humanizing of emotions, respect.

Do you see them, those gaunt, heart-sick women,
shoulder to shoulder, indomitable in the patient use
of their intelligence, in their long triumphant battle
against the weakness and evil in their own nature,
which were, as they had known from the first, the
only things in the world which could harm them?

What a race to belong to!

Well, then came the end, foreshadowed by weeks
of excited rumor, a confused, bewildered period of

guesses and half hopes, when nobody, not even the
guards, knew what was happening at the front. The
camp was all one crazy uproar, no newspaper, no
certainty of anything. Our little group of women
clung to each other, as the world rocked round them,
till the evening when the guards came running to
take them to the train. Not an instant to spare;
the thousands of other prisoners were yelling in the
riot which, the next day, tore the camp to pieces.
They huddled on their clothes and fled into the wild
confusion of the journey, standing up in locked cattle-cars, frantic to know what was happening, with
no idea in the world where they were or where the
train was taking them, until the moment when the
jolting cars stopped, the locked doors were broken
open and French voices out of the darkness cried,
"Mesdames, vous êtes chez vous!"

They were at home, at their own station, a faint
gray light showing the well-known pointed roofs of
their own city, the massive tower of the old Town
Hall black against the dawn. On the same platform,
where they had seen so many deported prisoners
return, vermin-ridden, filthy, half-imbecile, a burden
to themselves and their families, there they were,
lean and worn and pale, but stronger, better, finer
human beings than they had been before. Half-

awed by the greatness of their victory, they stood
there, like ghosts who had fought their way back
from the grave, peering out through the dim light
at their own homes.

That's where the story ought to end, oughtn't it?

But you know as well as I do that five years have
passed since that morning when they stood there,
awe-struck and transfigured. And I cannot conceal
the fact that I have seen them all again, a good
many times since then.

What are they doing with themselves now? Well,
the last time I made a round of visits among them,
I found the housewives concerned about their pre-
serves and the hang of their skirts; the business-
women deep in calculations about how to get around
the sinful rate of exchange. The mothers were
bringing up their children very hard, as we all do,
very much concerned about their knowing the children of the right people and no others. The teachers were grumbling about the delay in the promised
raise of their pay and complaining about the tyranny
of the Directrice of their Lycée. Young Mme.
Baudoin, now that her children are old enough to
go to school, often leaves them with the servants and
runs off to Brussels or Paris for a few days of fun.

All the returned hostages have grown quite stout, and they have taken up bridge whist with enthusiasm, once more.

As for Octavie, the last time I saw her, she was on fire with interest over a little green-house she was having built back of the kitchen, so that she might have fresh green vegetables the year around. It was very hard to achieve such a thing, what with the lack of workmen, the scarcity of bricks, and the high price of glass. But Octavie was sure she could manage it.

And so am I. Octavie can always manage anything she tries for.

OLD MAN WARNER

I MUST warn you at the outset that unless you or some of your folks came from Vermont, it is hardly worth your while to read about Old Man Warner. You will not be able to see anything in his story except, as we say in Vermont, a "gape and swallow" about nothing. Well, I don't claim much dramatic action for the story of old man Warner, but I am setting it down on the chance that it may fall into the hands of some one brought up on Vermont stories as I was. I know that for him there will be something in Old Man Warner's life, something of Vermont, something we feel and cannot express, as we feel the incommunicable aura of a personality.

The old man has been a weight on the collective mind of our town ever since I was a little girl, and that is a long time ago. He was an old man even then. Year after year, as our Board of Selectmen planned the year's town budget they had this worry about Old Man Warner, and what to do with him. It was not that old Mr. Warner was a dangerous character, or anything but strictly honest and law-abiding. But he had his own way of bothering his fellow citizens.

In his young days he had inherited a farm from his father, back up in Arnold Hollow, where at that time, about 1850, there was a cozy little settlement of five or six farms with big families. He settled there, cultivated the farm, married, and brought up a family of three sons. When the Civil War came, he volunteered together with his oldest boy, and went off to fight in the second year of the war. He came back alone in 1864, the son having fallen in the Battle of the Wilderness. And he went back up to Arnold Hollow to live and there he stayed, although the rest of his world broke up and re-arranged itself in a different pattern, mostly centering about the new railroad track in the main valley.

Only the older men returned to the Arnold Hollow settlement to go on cultivating their steep, rocky farms. The younger ones set off for the West, the two remaining Warner boys with the others. Their father and mother stayed, the man hardly ever leaving the farm now even to go to town. His wife said once he seemed to feel as though he never could get caught up on the years he had missed during the war. She said he always had thought the world of his own home.

The boys did pretty well out in Iowa, had the usual ups and downs of pioneer farmers, and by 1898, when their mother died, leaving their father alone at seventy-one, they were men of forty-eight and forty-six, who had comfortable homes to which to invite him to pass his old age.

Everybody in our town began to lay plans about what they would buy at the auction, when Old Man Warner would sell off his things, as the other Arnold Hollow families had. By this time, for one reason or another, the Warners were the only people left up there. The Selectmen planned to cut out the road up into Arnold Hollow, and put the tidy little sum saved from its upkeep into improvements on the main valley thoroughfare. But old Mr. Warner wrote his sons and told the Selectmen that he saw no reason for leaving his home to go and live in a strange place and be a burden to his children, with whom, having seen them at the rarest intervals during the last thirty years, he did not feel very well acquainted. And he always had liked his own home. Why should he leave it? It was pretty late in the day for him to get used to western ways. He'd just be a bother to his boys. He didn't want to be a bother to anybody, and he didn't propose to be!

There were a good many protests all round, but of course the Selectmen had not the faintest author-ity over him, and as quite probably his sons were at heart relieved, nothing was done. The town very grudgingly voted the money to keep up the Arnold Hollow road, but consoled itself by saying freely that the old cuss never had been so very bright and was worse now, evidently had no idea what he was trying to do, and would soon get tired of living alone and "doing for himself."

That was twenty-two years ago. Selectmen who were then vigorous and middle-aged, grew old, de-crepit, died, and were buried. Boys who were learn-ing their letters then, grew up, married, had chil-dren, and became Selectmen in their turn. Old Man Warner's sons grew old and died, and the names of most of his grand-children, scattered all over the West, were unknown to us. And still the old man lived alone in his home and "did for himself."

Every spring, when road work began, the Select-men groaned over having to keep up the Arnold Hollow road, and every autumn they tried their best to persuade the old man to come down to a set-tlement where he could be taken care of. Our town is very poor, and taxes are a heavy item in our calculations. It is just all we can do to keep our schools and roads going, and we grudge every penny we are forced to spend on tramps, paupers, or the indigent sick. Selectmen in whose régime town expenses were high, are not only never reëlected to town office, but their name is a by-word and a reproach for years afterwards. We elect them, among other things, to see to it that town expenses are not high, and to lay their plans accordingly.

Decades of Selectmen, heavy with this responsibility, tried to lay their plans accordingly in regard to Old Man Warner, and ran their heads into a stone wall. One Board of Selectmen after another knew exactly what would happen; the old dumb-head would get a stroke of paralysis, or palsy, or softening of the brain, or something, and the town Treasury would bleed at every pore for expensive medical service, maybe an operation at a hospital, and after that, somebody paid to take care of him. If they could only ship him off to his family! One of the granddaughters, now a middle-aged woman, kept up a tenuous connection with the old man, and answered, after long intervals, anxious communications from the Selectmen. Or if not that, if only they could get him down out of there in the winter, so they would not be saddled with the perpetual worry about what was happening to him, with the perpetual need to break out the snow in the road and go up there to see that he was all right.

But Old Man Warner was still not bright enough to see any reason why he should lie down on his own folks, or why he should not live in his own home. When gentle expostulations were tried, he always answered mildly that he guessed he'd rather go on living the way he was for a while longer; and when blustering was tried, he straightened up, looked the blusterer in the eye, and said he guessed there wasn't no law in Vermont to turn a man off his own farm, s'long's he paid his debts, and he didn't owe any that he knew of.

That was the fact, too. He paid spot cash for what he bought in his semi-yearly trips to the village to "do trading," as our phrase goes. He bought very little, a couple of pairs of overalls a year, a bag apiece of sugar, and coffee, and rice, and salt, and flour, some raisins, and pepper. And once or twice during the long period of his hermit life, an overcoat and a new pair of trousers. What he brought down from his farm was more than enough to pay for such purchases, for he continued to cultivate his land, less and less of it, of course, each year,

but still enough to feed his horse and cow and pig
and hens, and to provide him with corn and potatoes
and onions. He salted down and smoked a hog
every fall and ate his hens when they got too old
to lay.

And, of course, as long as he was actually eco-
nomically independent, the town, groaning with apprehension over the danger to its treasury though
it was, could not lay a finger on the cranky old
codger. And yet, of course, his economic independence couldn't last! From one day to the next,
something was bound to happen to him, something
that would cost the town money.

Each year the Selectmen planning the town ex-
penditures with the concentrated prudence born of
hard necessity, cast an uneasy mental glance up
Arnold Hollow way, and scringed at the thought that
perhaps this was the year when money would have
to be taken away from the road or the school fund
to pay for Old Man Warner's doctoring and nursing;
and finally for his burial, because as the years went
by, even the tenuous western granddaughter van-
ished: died, or moved, or something. Old Man
Warner was now entirely alone in the world.

All during my childhood and youth he was a
legendary figure of "sot" obstinacy and queerness.

We children used to be sent up once in a while, to take our turn in seeing that the old man was all right. It was an expedition like no other. You turned off the main road and went up the steep, stony winding mountain road, dense with the shade of sugar-maples and oaks. At the top, when your blown horse stopped to rest, you saw before you the grassy lane leading across the little upland plateau where the Arnold Hollow settlement had been. The older people said they could almost hear faint echoes of whetting scythes, and barking dogs, and cheerful homely noises, as there had been in the old days. But for us children there was nothing but a breathlessly hushed, sunny glade of lush meadows, oppressively silent and spooky, with a few eyeless old wrecks of abandoned farm houses, drooping and gray. You went past the creepy place as fast as your horse could gallop, and clattered into the thicket of shivering white birches which grew close to the road like a screen; and then—there was no sensation in my childhood quite like the coming out into the ordered, inhabited, humanized little clearing, in front of Old Man Warner's home. There were portly hens crooning around on the close-cropped grass, and a pig grunting sociably from his pen at you, and shining milk-pans lying in the sun tilted against the white birch sticks of the wood-pile, and Old Man Warner, himself, infinitely aged and stooped, in his faded, clean overalls, emerging from the barn-door to peer at you out of his bright old eyes and to give you a hearty, "Well, you're quite a long ways from home, don't you know it? Git off your horse, can't ye? I've got a new calf in here." Or perhaps if it were a Sunday, he sat in the sun on the front porch, with a clean shirt on, reading the weekly edition of the *New York Tribune*. He drove two miles every Saturday afternoon, down to his R. F. D. mail-box on the main road, to get this.

You heard so much talk about him down in the valley, so much fussing and stewing about his being so "sot," and so queer, that it always surprised you when you saw him, to find he was just like anybody else. You saw his calf, and had a drink of milk in his clean, well-scrubbed kitchen, and played with the latest kitten, and then you said good-by for that time, and got on your horse and went back through the birch thicket into the ghostly decay of the abandoned farms, back down the long, stony road to the valley where everybody was so cross with the unreasonable old man for causing them so much worry.

"How *could* he expect to go along like that, when

other old folks, so much younger than he, gave up and acted like other people, and settled down where you could take care of them! The house might burn down over his head, and he with it; or he might fall and break his hip and be there for days, yelling and fainting away till somebody happened to go by; or a cow might get ugly and hook him, and nobody to send for help." All these frightening possibilities and many others had been repeatedly presented to the old man himself with the elaborations and detail which came from heart-felt alarm about him. But he continued to say mildly that he guessed he'd go on living the way he was for a while yet.

"A *while!*" He was ninety years old.

And then he was ninety-one, and then ninety-two; and we were surer and surer he would "come on the town," before each fiscal year was over. At the beginning of last winter our Selectmen went up in a body to try to bully or coax the shrunken, wizened old man, now only half his former size, to go down to the valley. He remarked that he "guessed there wasn't no law in Vermont" and so forth, just as he had to their fathers. He was so old, that he could no longer straighten up as he said it, for his back was helplessly bent with rheumatism, and for lack

of teeth he whistled and clucked and lisped a good
deal as he pronounced his formula. But his meaning
was as clear as it had been thirty years ago. They
came sulkily away without him, knowing that they
would both be laughed at and blamed, in the valley,
because the cussed old crab had got the best of
them, again.

Last February, a couple of men, crossing over to
a lumber-job on Hemlock Mountain, by way of the
Arnold Hollow road, saw no smoke coming out of
the chimney, knocked at the door, and, getting no
answer, opened it and stepped in. There lay Old
Man Warner, dead on his kitchen floor in front of
his well-blacked cook-stove. The tiny, crooked, old
body was fully dressed, even to a fur cap and mittens, and in one hand was his sharp, well-ground ax.
One stove-lid was off, and a charred stick of wood
lay half in and half out of the fire box. Evidently
the old man had stepped to the fire to put in a stick
of wood before he went out to split some more, and
had been stricken instantly, before he could move a
step. His cold, white old face was composed and
quiet, just as it had always been in life.

The two lumbermen fed the half-starved pig and
hens and turned back to the valley with the news,

driving the old man's cow and horse in front of them; and in a couple of hours we all knew that Old Man Warner had died, all alone, in his own kitchen.

Well, what do you think! We were as stirred up about it—! We turned out and gave him one of the best funerals the town ever saw. And we put up a good marble tombstone that told all about how he had lived. We found we were proud of him, as proud as could be, the darned old bull-dog, who had stuck it out all alone, in spite of us. We brag now about his single-handed victory over old age and loneliness, and we keep talking about him to the children, just as we brag about our grandfather's victories in the Civil War, and talk to the children about the doings of the Green Mountain Boys. Old Man Warner has become history. We take as much satisfaction in the old fellow's spunk, as though he had been our own grandfather, and we spare our listeners no detail of his story: ". . . And there he stuck year after year, with the whole town plaguing at him to quit. And he earned his own living, and chopped his own wood, and kept himself and the house just as decent, and never got queer and frowzy and half-cracked, but stayed just like anybody, as nice an old man as ever you saw—all alone, all stark alone—beholden to nobody—asking no odds of anybody—yes, sir, and died with his boots on, at ninety-three, on a kitchen floor you could have et off of, 'twas so clean."

THE IDEAS OF M. BRODARD

DURING the first winter I spent in the boarding-school on the Rue de Vaugirard, the Brodard sisters were the mainstay of my life. It was not that I needed mainstaying in any of the regular classes, although we were driven like dogs by the grindingly thorough teachers, for lessons are lessons, wherever you find them, hard and tense though they may be in France, easy and loose in America. It was quite another part of our school life which routed me, the training in deportment and manners, carried on in three deadly sessions a week, by a wizened skipping old man, light and dry as a cork.

His little juiceless body was light, but everything else about him was heavy with the somber earnestness of his determination to teach us what he considered the manners of women of the world. Thrice a week we were obliged to begin those lessons by a ceremonious entry into the big salon, four by four, advancing in time to music across the bare shining desert of its waxed floors, counting furtively under our breaths, "one, two, three, four, glide, bend, recover, glide," as we courtesied to the Directrice, "advance again, one, two, three, four, glide, bend, recover, glide,"—here we saluted the Sous-Directrice —"advance again (I was always shaking partly with giggles at the absurdity of the whole business, partly with fear of the terrible eye of Professor Delacour), "one, two three, four, glide, bend . . ." but usually at this point of my attempted bow to the Professor of Deportment I was harshly told to go back and start the whole agonizing ritual over.

That was before the Brodard girls took me in hand and, flanking me on either side, swept me forward on the crest of their perfect advance and genuflection to the coveted place of safety on the other side of the room where, in a black-robed line, the little girls who had made a correct entry awaited further instructions in the manners of the world.

The support of the three Brodard girls did not stop short when they had engineered me through the matter of getting into a room. The professor himself was not more steeped in a religious sense of the importance of his instruction than were Madeleine, Lucie, and Clotilde Brodard. The insensate inner laughter which constantly threatened to shake the lid of my decorum, was safely muffled by their whole-souled attention as we stood there, watching

the elegant gestures and still more elegant immobili-
ties of Professor Delacour, as he explained the lesson of the day.

One day we were taught how to put money into
the contribution-box in church, "not with a preoccupied, bored air, nor yet with a complacent
smirk, but thus, gravely, with a quiet dignified gesture." Then he would pass the velvet contribution
bag down the line, and forty little girls must each
find the right expression, "not bored, or preoccupied,
not yet with a complacent, self-conscious look,
gravely—quietly—with dignity."

I can still feel in the pit of my stomach the quiver
of mingled terror and mirth with which at twelve
years of age, I prepared to be, "not bored or preoccupied, nor yet smirking and complacent, but quiet
—dignified—" I would never have lived through
it if I had not been hypnotized by the Brodard
girls.

Or perhaps we were required to be ladies stepping from a carriage and crossing a side-walk to
enter a theater, keenly conscious of the eyes of the
crowd on us; but required to seem unaware of spec-
tators, "graceful, moving with a well-bred repose,
and above all, unconscious, entirely natural and unconscious." Then two by two, squirmingly the cen-

ter of all the eyes in the salon, we crossed the imaginary sidewalk and entered the imaginary door, "quiet, graceful, above all unconscious, entirely natural and unconscious. . . ." Do you suppose for a moment I could have escaped annihilation at the hands of our High-Priest, if Clotilde Brodard had not been my fellow acolyte, applying all her orthodox convictions to the problem set before us?

Yes, the Brodard girls were an example to us all, in and out of the class in deportment, for they were as scrupulously observant of all the rules of good behavior in daily school-life as under the eye of Professor Delacour. Any chance observer would have been sure that they were preparing to enter the wealthiest and most exclusive society, an impression by no means contradicted by the aspect of their mother, a quiet, distinguished, tailored person, who brought them to school at the beginning of the term, and once in a while made the tiresome trip from Morvilliers to Paris to see them. But the Brodards must have had some training in genuine good-breeding as well as the quaint instruction given by Professor Delacour, for they never made any pretensions to wealth or social standing—they said very little of any sort about their home life.

Two years later I spent my Christmas vacation

with them, and at once I understood a good deal
more about them.   Young as I was—fourteen at
the time—it was plain to me as it would have been
to any observer, that they took their lessons in "society manners" so seriously because society manners
and any occasions for using them were the only
things lacking in the home where they were so comfortable, so much loved, and so well cared for.
They lived on a shabby street in Morvilliers, in a
small apartment, with one maid-of-all-work; and although their mother had a genius for keeping everything on a plane of strict gentility, their big, gay,
roughly clad, unceremonious father was the ramping red editor of the most ramping red radical
newspaper in that part of France, the center of all
the anti-everything agitations going on in the region.

As used to happen in Europe, in the far-gone
days, when I was fourteen years old (but not at all
as it happens now-a-days) what they called ramping
and redness looked very plain and obvious to an
American.   Most of what M. Brodard was making
such a fuss about, seemed to me just what everybody at home took for granted: for instance his
thesis that every man ought to earn his own living
no matter how high his social position might be.   I
was astonished that anybody could consider that a

revolutionary idea. Among other things, M. Brodard was what people would call now-a-days a femi-
nist, expounding hotly his conviction that women
should be trusted with the responsibility for the conduct of their own lives, and the earning of their own
livings. These opinions found no echo at all in the
serious-minded middle-class families of his town, nor
indeed in his family, but they were an old story to
me. I told him as much, informing him confidently
from my wide experience as a child in the impecuni-
ous faculty of a western State-University, that
everybody in America expected as a matter of course
to earn his *and* her own living—everybody! He accepted this as unquestioningly as I advanced it, with
the fresh faith and enthusiasm which upheld him in
all the generous quixotism of his life. I believe, indeed, that on the strength of my testimony he actually wrote some editorials about America in his furiously convinced style.

Of course he was the champion of the working
classes as against the bourgeoisie, adored by the
first and hated by the second. It was an adventure
to walk with him along the narrow, cobbled streets
of the musty little town. Everywhere the lean,
sinewy men in working clothes and the thin women
in aprons and without hats, had a quick, flashing

look of pleasure to see his great frame come strid-
ing vigorously along. Everywhere the artisans
stopped their work to call a hearty greeting to him,
or to step quickly to meet him, full of some grievance, sure of his sympathy, and comforted by the
quick flame of his indignation. And everywhere the
very sight of him put a taste of green apples into the
mouths of all the well-dressed people. You could
see that by the sour expression of their broad, florid
faces. The prosperous merchant at the door of his
shop frowned, cleared his throat, and turned hastily
within doors, as he saw M. Brodard come marching
along, humming a tune, his hat cocked light-heartedly over one ear. The lawyer in his black broadcloth coat passed us hurriedly; the women in expensive furs stepped high, drew their long skirts
about them, and looked him straight in the eye, with
an expression half fear, half horror. This last
made him break out into the hearty, full-throated
laugh, always close to the surface with him
—the laugh that was as characteristic a part of him
as the shape of his nose.

I understood now why Mme. Brodard sent the
girls away to school. They would have been outcasts in any bourgeoise school in their own town.
Yet M. Brodard was a great champion of the pub-

lic schools and never lost an opportunity of defend-
ing against their bitter critics the public lycées for
girls, then just struggling into being in France. I
wondered a little that he should allow his daughters to go to such a boarding-school as ours. But
it seemed that the angry resistance of the moneyed
and pious families of Morvilliers had up to that
time prevented the establishment of a public lycée
for girls there. This enabled Mme. Brodard to
steer past another dangerous headland in the complicated course of her life. Perhaps, also, warm-
hearted M. Brodard was not inclined to be too hard
on his girls, whom he fondly loved, after the adoring
manner of French fathers, nor to expect too much
from his devoted wife in the way of conforming to
his ideas.

Even at that time, poor Mme. Brodard's life was
all one miracle of adroit achievement in reconciling
irreconcilable elements and effecting impossible com-
promises. She had married her husband when they
were both young (he must have been an irresistible
suitor), and before his hot-headed sympathies for
the under-dog had absorbed him. Like a good and
devoted French wife, she never admitted that anything her Bernard did was other than what she
would wish. But she remained exactly what she

had been at the time of her marriage, and although
she was deeply attached to her kind and faithful
husband and made the best of homes for him, she
had not the slightest intention of changing a hair
or becoming anything but a good bourgeoise, a devoted believer in social distinctions, in the Church,
in the laboring classes *as such and in their places,*
and above all in the excellence of owning property
and inheriting money.

On this last point M. Brodard went much further
than anything I had heard discussed at home, and
poured out incessantly in brilliant editorials a tor-
rent of scorn, laughter, hatred, and denunciation,
upon the sacred institution of inheritance, the very
keystone of the French social edifice. "How ridiculous," he used to write on mornings when no other
forlorn hope stood in special need of a harebrained
charge, "that the mere chance of birth, or a personal
caprice, should put vast sums of unearned wealth
into the hands of a man who has not had the slightest connection with its production. Property, the
amassing of wealth by a man who has had the acu-
men and force to produce it . . . we may have two
opinions about that, about whether he should be allowed to keep for himself all he can lay his hands
on. But there can be no two opinions about the

hilarious idiocy of the theory that his grown-up son has any inherent right to possess that wealth, his son who has no more to do with it than the Emperor of China, save by a physiological accident. A hundred years from now, people will be laughing at our imbecile acquiescence in such a theory, as we now laugh at the imbecile acquiescence of whole provinces and kingdoms in the Middle Ages, passed from the hand of one master to another, because somebody had married somebody else."

Mme. Brodard used to say resignedly, that she minded such editorials least of all. "That is a principle that will never touch *our* lives!" she said with melancholy conviction, for her modest dowry was the extent of their fortune and of their expectations. She herself had been an orphan and all the Brodard elders were dead, having left nothing to the family of such an enemy to society as they considered Bernard to be.

She did not complain; she never complained of anything her husband did; but it was plain to see that she thought it her obvious duty to protect her daughters from the consequences of their dear father's ideas. The income from her dowry kept them at school and dressed them at home, and as the oldest began to approach the marriageable age

Mme. Brodard cast about her with silent intensity for some possible means for stretching that dowry to enable Madeleine to make the right sort of match. She knew of course that this was an impossible undertaking; but all her married life had been an impossible undertaking carried through to success, and she did not despair, although there were times when she looked white and anxious.

But this was never when M. Brodard was at home. Indeed it was impossible for any one to be tense or distraught in the sunny gaiety of M. Brodard's presence. His entrance into that neat, hushed, narrow, waxed, and polished interior was like the entrance of a military band playing a quick-step. He was always full of his latest crusade, fired with enthusiasms, hope, and certainty of success. He made you feel that he was the commanding officer of a devoted force, besieging an iniquitous old enemy, and every day advancing further toward victory. Yet another blast, down would tumble the flimsy walls of cowardly traditional injustice, and sunshine would stream into the dark places!

Full of faith in what he was doing, he was as light-hearted as a boy, electrifying the most stagnant air with the vibrant current of his conviction that life is highly worth the trouble it costs. Big girls as we were, he swept us off into hilarious games of hide-and-seek; and never in any later evenings of my life have I rocked in such gales of fun as on the evenings when we played charades. An impersonation of a fussy, clucking setting hen which he gave as part of the word, "ampoule" has remained with me as a high-water mark of sheer glorious foolery never surpassed by the highest-salaried clown. In the following charade we laughed so at his "creation" of a fateful Napoleon that we could not sit on our chairs; and after that, carried away by his own high spirits, he did the "strong man" at the village fair (he was a prodigiously powerful athlete) lifting a feather with a grotesque display of swelling muscles, clenched jaws, and widespread legs which all but finished me. The tears of mirth used to come to my eyes as I recalled that evening, and many a taut, high-strung moment of my adolescence in after years relaxed into healthy amusement at the remembered roar of M. Brodard's laughter.

M. Brodard's laughter . . . alas!

And yet at the very time when his care-free, fearless laughter so filled my ears, he was standing out single-handed against the most poisonous hostility, to force an investigation of a framed-up law case, in which a workingman had been defrauded of his

rights. Apparently there was always some such
windmill against which he thought it necessary to
charge. Apparently his zeal for forlorn hopes never
diminished. We went back to school after that vacation leaving him the center of a pack of yelling
vituperations from all the staid and solid citizens of
the region . . . "poor, dear Papa," as the Brodard girls always said, imitating their mother's accent.

To me, school and lessons in deportment seemed
queerer than ever, after that great gust of stormy,
ruffling wind, but the Brodard girls were used to
such contrasts. They but plunged themselves deeper
than ever, up to their very necks, into the atmosphere of gentility. They had caught more than their
mother's accent, they had caught her deep anxiety
about their future, her passionate determination
that the ideas of their father should not drag them
into that impossible world of workingmen, radicals
and badly dressed outcasts, which was the singular
choice of their excellent poor dear Papa.

When Mme. Brodard came to Paris, in the well-
cut tailored dress which I now knew to be the only
one she possessed, she reported that Papa, by sheer
capacity for shouting unpleasant truths at the top
of his great voice, had obtained a re-trial and acquit-

tal of that tiresome workingman, and was now off
on a new tack, was antagonizing all the merchants
of town by an exposé of their grinding meanness
to their hapless employees. It seemed that libel-
suits were thick in the air, and the influential members of society crossed to the other side of the street
when they met M. Brodard. "But you know how
poor dear Papa seems to thrive on all that!"

Well, *he* might thrive on all that, but Madeleine,
Lucie, and Clotilde knew very well that nothing
they wanted would thrive on "all that." Their only
salvation was in escape from it. In the effort to
prepare themselves for that escape, they smeared
themselves, poor things, from head to foot with good
breeding. They had nothing but themselves,
Maman, and her little dowry to count on; but at
least no one should be able to guess from their manners that their home life had not been conventional.
Mme. Brodard went on, that day, to consult with
her banker about re-investing some of her little fortune, so that it would mean more income. When
Madeleine left school, they would need more, Heaven
knew, to piece out the plain living furnished by the
head of the house. What could they do to rise to
that crisis? *When Madeleine left school* . . . an
abyss before their feet! Could they perhaps go

south, to a winter resort for a few months every year, where there were no Morvilliers people, where there might be eligible young men . . . or even some not so young? They all looked anxious and stern, when they thought of it, for after Madeleine, there were Lucie and Clotilde!

I was sent home to America in June that year, before the end of the school-term. The good-bys were said at lunch-time, before my schoolmates went off to the lesson in deportment. The last I saw of the Brodards at the time, was through the door of the salon as I passed on my way to the street. They were learning how to handle a fan, how to open it—"not tearing it open with both hands like a peasant girl, but flirting it open with a sinuous bend of the wrist of one hand . . . not so abrupt! . . . smooth, suave, with an aristocratic . . ." As I went down the hall, the voice of Professor Delacour died away on these words. I wondered what poor dear Papa was up to now.

Two years later when I was taken back to France and went to visit the Brodards, I found that he was still up to the same sort of thing. Just then he was making the echoes yell in the defense of a singularly unattractive, snuffy old man, who lived in a village six or seven kilometers away from Morvilliers. Old

M. Duval, it seemed, had gone to South America in, his youth, had accumulated some property there, and had lost his religion. Now, at sixty-nine, with so it was said, enough money to live on, he had come back to Fressy, had bought a comfortable little home there, and settled down to end his days in his birth-place. But Fressy, as it happened, had always been and still was noted for its piety and conservatism. The curé of the parish was a man of flaming zeal, and the Mayor was also a very devout ultramon-tane. Till then their influence had been unques-tioned in the town. They had boasted that there was one loyal village left in France where none of the poisonous new ideas had come in to corrupt the working classes, and to wean them from their duti-ful submission to the rule of their spiritual and secu-lar betters. Apparently till then, M. Brodard had overlooked the existence of such a village near him.

His attention was now very much called to it by the persecution of old M. Duval. The persistent and ostentatious absence from Mass of the returned traveler was follower by a shower of stones which broke most of his windows. His easy-going advice given publicly in a café to some young workmen of the town to follow his example, to stand up for themselves, get higher wages or strike, was answered by the poisoning of his dog. The old fellow became indignant, and never dreaming of the heat of the feeling against him, walked straight up to M. le Curé one day in the street, and asked him—as if the priest had anything to do with what was happening!—whether the laws of France did or did not permit a man to live quietly in his own house, no matter what his opinions were! That night some anonymous defender of the status quo set fire to his chicken-house. It was at this time that M. Brodard began to be aware of the existence of Fressy.

Old M. Duval called on the police for protection. "The police." That sounds very fine, but the police of Fressy meant a solitary old garde-champêtre whose wife was the most pious woman in town, and whose only daughter was the cook in the house of the fiercely legitimatist Mayor. It is not surprising that the next morning, the scoffing unbeliever from overseas found that somehow marauders had eluded "the police," and laid waste his promising kitchen-garden. They intended (they proclaimed it openly) to drive out from their sanctified midst, the man who flaunted his prosperity as the result of a wicked and godless life.

But they had not counted on M. Brodard and on his unparalleled capacity for making a noise. He stormed out to Fressy to see the old man, thoroughly frightened by this time; heard his story, exploding at intervals into fiery rockets of indignation; clasped him in his arms, as though M. Duval had been his own kin; and swore that he would prove to him that justice and freedom existed in France to-day as always. The old man's nerves were shaken by his troubled nights and his harried sense of invisible enemies all about him. Until that moment it had seemed to him that all the world was against him. His relief was immense. He returned M. Brodard's embrace emotionally, his trembling old arms clasped hard about M. Brodard's great neck, the tears in his scared old eyes.

Then M. Brodard hurried back to Morvilliers, tore the throttle open, and let her go . . . to the great discomfort of Mme. Brodard and the girls, the two elder of whom were now very reluctantly preparing themselves to teach, for they had not been able to organize the longed-for escape. That was the situation when I visited them.

Of course in due time the intemperate publicity about the matter put an end to the attacks on M. Duval. The rattling crackle of M. Brodard's quick-fire protests rose in the air, till they reached the ears of the Sous-Prefect, from whose exalted office orders to "see to that matter" were issued, and came with imperative urgence even to the royalist Mayor of Fressy. He very grudgingly issued certain unofficial orders, which meant quiet in old M. Duval's life. There was even a victim sacrificed to shut M. Brodard's too-articulate mouth. The garde-champêtre lost his position and his chance for a pension, which was very hard on an excellent, honest man whose only intention had been to do his duty as he saw it.

By the time that I was back in America in college, Clotilde wrote me that all that disturbance had died down, that M. Duval, horrid old thing, had come on his shaking old legs to make a visit to Papa, to thank him with deep emotion for the intense peace and comfort of his present life. I could read between the lines that Clotilde thought they might very well have a little more of those commodities in their own life.

After that I heard from some one else (for M. Brodard and his ideas were becoming famous) that the opposition had finally caught him in a legal technicality, something connected with his campaign for tearing down the miserable old disease-soaked medieval hovels where many poor people lived in Morvilliers. The proprietors of the threatened rookeries chipped in together, hired expensive expert legal advice, and finally, to their immense satisfaction, succeeded in getting a tiny sentence of imprisonment, for defamation of their characters, inflicted on M. Brodard. He was kept in jail for two weeks, I believe, which was a fortnight of pure glory. All his humble adherents, hundreds of them, came tramping in to see him from all the region round, bringing tribute. His "cell" was heaped with flowers, he fared on the finest game and fattest poultry, and . . . what pleased him vastly more . . . the fiery editorials which he sent out from his prison about the infamy of wretched lodgings for poor families were noticed and reprinted everywhere in France, where the circumstances of his grotesque imprisonment were known.

The condemnation which his opponents meant to be a crushing disgrace turned out an apotheosis. He enjoyed every moment of it and emerged from his two weeks vacation, ruddier, stronger, in higher spirits than ever, his name shining with the praise of generous-hearted men all over the country. He cocked his hat further over one ear than ever and strode off home. You could fairly see the sparks fly from beneath his feet.

. . . .

The morning after his release from prison, news came from Fressy that old M. Duval had died of apoplexy.

Well, what of that?   Ah, what of that . . .?

He had willed his whole fortune to M. Brodard, and it seemed he was frightfully rich: it came to more than three million francs.

.   .   .   .

Oh, yes, he took it. Of course he did. You knew he would. What else would you have had him do? It's all very well to have abstract ideas about the absurdity and iniquity of inheritance; but when your own daughters . . . and your own wife . . . expect so confidently . . .

Mme. Brodard, you see . . . he was devoted to his wife who had so faithfully made the best of homes for him; and to his daughters whom he loved so dearly. . . .

Can't you see the astounded radiance of their faces at the news?   And they'd already been sacrificed so many years for his ideas. . . . *Ideas!*

What do you suppose he could do but accept it?

.   .   .   .

I don't know one thing about the inner history of this period when M. Brodard was bringing himself to a decision, and in the light of a glimpse, just one glimpse which I had later, I think the less I know about it the better for my peace of mind. The only information I had was contained in a very nice, conventional note from Mme. Brodard, giving me, in the pleasantly formal, well-turned phrases of French epistolatory style, the news of their great good fortune which, she said, was certainly sent by Providence to protect her dear husband from the suffering and hardship which would have been his without it; for M. Brodard was very ill, she wrote, oh, very ill indeed! He had gone through a phase of strange mental excitement; from that he had sunk into melancholia which had frightened them, and in the end had succumbed to a mysterious malady of the nervous system which made him half-blind and almost helpless. Helpless . . . her wonderful, strong husband! What could she have done to care for him if it had not been for this financial windfall coming just when it was most needed?

You can imagine my stupefaction on reading this letter. It was caused as much by learning that M. Brodard was a hopeless invalid as by learning about that odd business of the fortune left them. How strange! M. Brodard with a nervous affection which left him in a wheel chair! It was incredible. I reread the beautifully written letter, try-

ing hard to see if anything lay between the lines.
But there was nothing more in it than I had already found. It was evidently written in the utmost good faith. Everything Mme. Brodard did
was done with the utmost good faith.

Some years later I was in France again and found
myself near the address on the Riviera where the
Brodards had purchased an estate. I had not heard
from them in some months, but on the chance that
they might be there, I went over from Mentone on
a slow way-train which, returning three hours later,
would give me time to pay my call and get back the
same afternoon. Everybody at the little white-stuc-
coed station knew where the Brodard villa was, and
when he knew where I was going, the driver of the
shabby cab tucked me into it with a respect for my
destiny he had noticeably not shown to my very
plain and rather dusty traveling-dress. We climbed
a long hill-road to a high point, commanding a glorious view of the brilliant sea and yet more brilliant
coast, and turned into a long manorial allée of fine
cypress trees.

The house was as manorial and imposing as the
avenue leading to it and I began to be uneasily aware
of my plain garb. As I went up the steps to the
great door I could feel the house thrilling rhythmi-

cally to excellent music, and to the delicate gliding
of many finely-shod feet.

A servant led me to a small round salon hung
with blue brocade, and in a moment Mme. Brodard
came hurrying to meet me. She had bloomed herself luxuriantly open like a late rose, and from head
to foot was a delight to the eye. Of course she was
very much surprised to see me, but with never a
glance at my garb she gave me the cordial welcome
of an old friend. Her perfect good faith and good
breeding still governed her life, it was plain to see.
She was giving a *thé dansant* for the younger girls,
she told me, adding that Madeleine had been married two months before to a silk manufacturer of
Lyons. She was evidently glad to see me, but naturally enough, just for the moment, a little puzzled
what to do with me! I suggested to her relief that
I make a visit to M. Brodard first of all and wait
to see the others till their guests had gone.

"Yes, that's the very thing," she said, ringing for
a servant to show me the way, "he'll remember you,
of course. He will be so glad to see you. He always liked you so much."

As the servant came to the door, she added with a
note of caution. "But you must expect to find him
sadly changed. His health does not improve, al-

though we have a resident physician for him, and *everything* is done for him, poor dear Bernard!"

The servant in a quiet livery of the finest materials, led me upstairs over velvet carpets, and then upstairs again, to a superb room at the top of the house. It was all glass towards the miraculous living blue of the Mediterranean, and full of flowers, books, and harmoniously designed modern furniture. M. Brodard, clad in a picturesque, furred dressing-gown sat in a wheel chair, his bald head sunk on his breast, his eyes fixed and wide-open, lowered towards his great, wasted white hands lying empty on his knees. Until he raised his eyes to look at me, I could not believe that it was he . . . no, it was not possible!

He remembered me, as Mme. Brodard had predicted, but the rest of her simple-hearted prophecy did not come true. He was not in the least glad to see me and made not the slightest pretense that he was. A look that was intolerable to see, had come into his eyes as he recognized me, and he had instantly turned his head as though he hated the sight of me.

I knew at once that I ought to get out of the room, no matter how; but I was so stricken with horror and pity that for a moment I could not collect myself, and stood there stupidly.

A faint distant sound of gay music hummed rhythmically in the silence. A professional-looking man who had been sitting with a book on the other side of the room got up now and, with the bored air of a man doing his duty, took hold of M. Brodard's thin wrist to feel the pulse.

M. Brodard snatched away his hand and said to me over the doctor's head, "Well, you see how it is with us now." He corrected himself. "You see how it is with me."

His accent, his aspect, his eyes added what he did not say. He had been trembling with impatience because I was there at all. Now he was trembling with impatience because I did not answer him! His terrible eyes dared me to answer.

I would have done better to hold my tongue altogether, but my agitation was so great that I lost my head. I felt that I was called upon to bring out something consoling, and heard myself murmuring in a foolish babble something or other about possible compensations for his illness, about his still being able to go on with his work, to write, to publish, in that way to propagate his ideas. . . .

At that he burst into a laugh I would give anything in the world not to have heard.

"My ideas . . . ha! ha! ha!" he cried.

Oh, I got myself out of the room then! I ran down the velvet carpets of the stairs, my hands over my ears.

As I hurried along to the outside door I passed the salon. I saw, across the bare, gleaming desert of its waxed floor, Clotilde standing with a well-dressed man. She had a fan in her hand, and, as I looked, she opened it deftly, with a sinuous bend of her flexible wrist . . . "smoothly, suavely . . . with an aristocratic . . ."

FAIRFAX HUNTER

THE erratic philanthropist of our family arrived from New York one spring day with a thin, sickly-looking, middle-aged, colored man, almost in rags. "This is Fairfax Hunter," he announced with the professional cheeriness of the doer of good. "He's pretty badly run down and needs country air. I thought maybe you could let him sleep in the barn, and work around enough for his board."

There was nothing professionally or in any other way cheery about the colored man, who stood waiting indifferently for my decision, his knees sagging, his hollow chest sunken. As I glanced at him he raised his dark, blood-shot eyes and met my look. I decided hastily, on impulse, from something in the expression of his eyes, that we could not send him away.

I led him off to the barn and showed him the corner of the hay-mow where the children sometimes sleep when our tiny house overflows with guests. He sank down on it and closed his eyes. The lids were blue and livid as though bruised. He had nothing with him except the ragged clothes on his back.

When I returned to the house, the philanthropist explained that Fairfax was a Virginia negro—"You could tell that from his name, of course"—who had come to New York and fallen into bad ways, "drink, etc. . . . But there's something about him. . . ."

Yes, I agreed to that. There was something about him. . . .

Fairfax lived with us after this for more than four years, the last years of his life. He was really very ill at first, the merest little flicker of life puffing uncertainly in and out of the bag of skin and bones which was his body. The doctor said that rest and food were the only medicines for him. He lay like a piece of sodden driftwood for long hours on the edge of the hay where the sun caught it.

The good-natured old Yankee woman who was cooking for me then, used to take him out big bowls of fresh milk, and slices of her home-baked bread, and stand chatting with him while he sat up listlessly and ate. At least, she being a great gossip, did the chattering, and Fairfax listened, once in a while murmuring the soft, slow, "Ye-e-s 'm," which came to be the speech he was known by, in our valley.

He seemed to have no interest in getting well, but little by little the sunshine, the quiet, the mountain air, and something else of which we did not dream till later, lifted him slowly up to health. He began to work a little in the garden, occasionally cut the grass around the house and, borrowing the carpentering tools, built himself a little room in the corner of the barn. One day I paid him a small sum for his services about the place, and my husband gave him some old clothes. The next afternoon he took his first walk to the village, and came back with a pipe and a bag of tobacco. That evening Nancy, our "help," called me to the kitchen window and pointed out towards the barn. On a bench before the barn door sat Fairfax, smoking, his head tipped back, watching the moon sink behind the mountain. We agreed that it looked as though he were getting well.

Nancy had to go home to a sick sister that Fall, and Fairfax moved into the kitchen to occupy her place. It came out that he had once worked in a hotel kitchen in Virginia, so that thereafter our Vermont cookstove turned out Southern food, from hot biscuit to fried chicken.

There is very little caste feeling in our valley,

and not a bit of color prejudice. Many of our people had never even seen a negro to speak to before they knew Fairfax, and they liked him very much.

He always was very thin, but he had filled out a little by this time; had gone to a dentist by my advice and had the blackened stumps of his teeth replaced by shining new ivories; had bought with his first wages a new suit of clothes, and was considered by our farmer families to be "quite a good-looking fellow." He kept his curling gray hair cut short to his head, his thin cheeks scrupulously shaven, and was always presentable.

As a matter of course he was invited to all the country gatherings, like other people's "hired help," along with the rest of us. I remember the first of these invitations: some one telephoned from the village to announce a church supper, and I was urged, "Do bring down a good crowd. We've got a lot of food to dispose of."

I stepped back into the kitchen and told Fairfax not to get supper that night, as we were all going to the village to a church supper.

"Yes'm," said Fairfax.

"I want you to be ready to start at a quarter to six," I added, glancing at the clock.

"Who, *me?*" said Fairfax, with a little start.

"Yes," I answered, a little surprised. "Didn't you hear me say I wanted us all to go?"

Fairfax looked at me searchingly, "Where'll I get my supper?"

"Why, they usually have the church suppers out on the church green unless it rains, and then they go down to the basement rooms."

Fairfax said apathetically, "No'm, they don't want me."

I saw now what was in his mind, and said, to set him right, "Oh, yes, they do. You know the people around here haven't any of those notions. Come on."

"No'm, they don't want me," he repeated.

I beckoned him to follow me, went back to the telephone and rang up the woman who was arranging for the supper. "Do you want me to bring Fairfax Hunter with us?" I asked her explicitly.

"Why, of course," she said surprised. "I told you we want a crowd."

After this Fairfax stood undecided, his sensitive face clouded and anxious. I had a glimpse then of the long years of brutal discrimination through which he had lived, and said, feeling very much ashamed of my civilization, "Now, Fairfax, don't be so foolish. We *want* you to go. Get on your best clothes, so's to do honor to the Ladies Aid."

He went back to the room in the corner of the barn, and half an hour later came out, fresh and neat in his new suit, closely shaven, his slim yellow hands clean, his gray hair smooth. He looked almost eager, with a light in his eyes that was like a distant reflection of gaiety. But when we cranked up the Ford to go he was not in sight. We called him, and he answered from the barn that he was not ready, and would walk in. I was vexed, and shouted back as we rolled down the hill, "Now don't fail to come."

It rained on the way in, and the supper was served in the basement, with all the neighbors spruced up and fresh, while the busy women of the Ladies Aid rushed back and forth bringing us salmon loaf, pickles, Boston brown bread, creamed potatoes, and coffee and ice-cream as from the beginning of time they always have; but though I kept a chair at our table empty for Fairfax, and sat where I could watch the door, he did not appear.

After the supper I went across the street to see my aunt, house-ridden with a hard cold. She told me that from her windows she had seen Fairfax come down to the village street, halt in front of the church, go on, turn back, halt again. She said he had paced back and forth in this way for half an hour, and finally had gone home.

When we reached the house we found Fairfax there, his good clothes put away, his cook's white apron tied around him, eating bread and butter and cold meat.

I sat down to scold him for not doing as I had said. When I had finished Fairfax looked at me, hesitated, and said, "If it had been out of doors, maybe I'd have tried it." There was an expression on his thin somber face, which made me get up and go away without venturing any more comment.

As his health increased, his spirits rose somewhat. My little son was born that winter, and Fairfax was very fond of the baby, who soon developed the most extravagant fondness for his company. When spring came on, and gardening arrived, Fairfax took over a part of that work, and had a long-running feud with the woodchucks who live in the edge of the woods beyond our garden patch. It was a quaint sight to see Fairfax in his white jacket and apron, sitting outside the kitchen door, peeling potatoes, a rifle across his knees, or to see him emerge in a stealthy run from the kitchen door, gun in hand, and

dart across the road to get a better sight on the little brown garden thieves. It did me good to see him
stirred up enough to care about anything.

He turned out to be a great reader and worked
his way through most of our library. I know you
will not believe me when I tell you who his favorite
author was. But I am not concerned with seeming
probable, only with telling the truth. It was Thomas
Hardy, whose philosophy of life fitted in exactly
with Fairfax's views and experience. He was no
talker and rarely said anything to me beyond the
gentle "no'm" and "yes'm" with which he received
orders. But once he remarked to my husband that
Thomas Hardy certainly did know what life was
like. He went straight through that entire set of
novels, once he had found them on the shelves, and
all that winter my life was tinged with the consciousness of Fairfax sitting in the kitchen after his
work was done, deep in communion with Hardy.
Our visiting friends used to find the sight so curious
as to be amusing. I did not find it so.

The neighbors grew very used to him, and being
sociable, friendly people, with a great deal of Yankee
curiosity about the rest of the world, they often
tried to get Fairfax to tell about life in the south.
When he went out for a stroll in the evening, they

would call to him, from where they were weeding a
bed in the garden, or giving the pigs their last meal,
"Hello, there, Fairfax, come on in for a minute." If
they were in the yard, or on the porch, Fairfax
often accepted the invitation. As we went by in
the car we used to see him leaning up against the
porch-railing, talking, or helping some busy woman
set out her cabbage plants. But he never went indoors.

Our corner of the valley is a very cheerful one
with a number of lively children to keep us from
"shucking over" into middle age too soon, and the
school-house is often the place where we gather for
good times. The school-benches are pushed back,
the lamps lighted, the fiddler tunes up, and we all
dance, young and old, children and grown-ups.
Fairfax was invited as a matter of course to these
informal affairs, and some of the children who were
very fond of the kind, gentle, silent man, used to
pull at his coat, and say, "Do come on in, Mr.
Hunter! Dance with me!" But Fairfax only grinned
uneasily and shook his head. He used to stand
outside, smoking his pipe and looking in wistfully
at the brightly lighted room. As we skipped back
and forth in the lively old-fashioned dances, we
could see him, a dim shape outside the window, the

little red glow of his pipe reflected once in a while from his dark, liquid eyes. Sometimes when the window was open, he came and leaned his elbows on the sill, nodding his head with the music, and beating time lightly with his fingers, his eyes following us about as we stepped back and forth in the complicated figures.

When we were ready to serve the "refreshments," some of us went out into the entry-way, and Fairfax came in to help us with the uncomfortable work of digging out the ice and salt from the top of the freezers, and opening the cans. I used to say at first, "Fairfax, why don't you go in and dance, too? Anybody can see you know just how to." But his invariable answer, "No'm, I guess I won't," had in it a quality which ended by silencing me.

The older people called him Fairfax, as we did, but because he was a grown man, and a middle-aged man, they thought it not good manners for the children to call him by his first name, and taught the boys and girls to call him Mr. Hunter. We thought this perfectly natural, and none of us, entirely ignorant of Southern ways, had the slightest idea of what this meant to him.

Once a year, Fairfax took a two weeks' vacation, and all his earnings for the year. He went off to the city, clean, and strong, and well-dressed; and he always came back without a cent, sick, and coughing, and shabby, with a strong smell of whiskey all over him. Of course, we took him severely to task for this inexcusable behavior, getting out for his benefit all the accepted axioms of conduct, prudence, ambition, self-interest, and so on, showing him how he could save his money, and put it in the bank, and be prosperous.

He always answered with his invariable soft, "Yes'm," except on one occasion, the last year of his life, when he said somberly, with his soft, Southern accent, "I've got no use for money. I can't buy *what I want*. I'm a colored man."

We learned more about him . . . a little . . . that he had a sister now married to a sober, hardworking carpenter, living in Buffalo, that he had lived at home with his mother till long after he was grown up, working in the hotel, and supporting them both with his wages. That was the only time I ever saw him show emotion. His thin face suddenly twisted like a child's, and tears shone in his eyes. "She was an awful good woman, my mother was. She had a terrible time to get along when my sister and I were little. She never had a husband to help her. My father was a white man."

"Fairfax, why don't you think of marrying and having a home of your own?" I said impulsively.

"To bring up children to be Jim-Crowed?" he asked, shortly.

On another occasion, when I was commenting on the singular excellence of his writing and figuring, I heard about his school taught by a northern Negro, who had gone down south as a volunteer teacher after the war. It was from him that Fairfax had learned his correct speech, without a trace of what we call the Negro dialect.

When the war in Europe came, and we decided to take the children and go to France we were confronted with the question of what to do with Fairfax. He wanted to go with us, and asked for it with more insistence than he ever showed, and I often now regret that I did not try to take him. But it seemed impossible to add to the responsibility of little children in a war-ridden country, the heavier responsibility in a country flowing with alcohol, for a man with a weakness for drink. Besides, we could not afford the extra expense.

There was no place for him in our region, where few people keep help in the kitchen. In the hurry and confusion of our preparations for departure I simply could not think of anything satisfactory to do in the United States of America for a proud sensitive colored man. The best I could devise was to find him a place with a friend, unfortunately in a city where there were plenty of saloons and plenty of race prejudice. I can't see now why I did not think of Canada. But we knew no one in Canada.

When we separated, he kissed the children good-by, seriously, and shook the hand which I held heartily out to him. After our last words, I said, making a great effort to break through the wall of dignified reserve which his silence built around him, "Fairfax, do keep straight, won't you?"

He looked at me with that passive, neutral look of his, which had to my eye an ironical color, and made a little gesture with his shoulders and eyebrows that might mean anything.

He drank himself to death inside six months. I read the news in a letter from his sister, the first and only letter I ever had from her. I had hurried back to the apartment in Paris one evening to be with the children during an air-raid, found the American mail arrived, and read it to the accompaniment of that anti-aircraft bombardment which was so familiar a part of the war to make the world safe for democracy. My letter from the country of democ-

racy informed me that Fairfax had died, alone, before his sister could reach him. "He had been
drinking again, I am afraid, from what they told
me. I always felt so bad about Fairfax drinking,
but he wouldn't stop—he was just plain discouraged
of life. He never touched a drop as long as our
mother was living. He was always so sorry for our
mother, and so good to her, though she was only a
poor ignorant woman, who couldn't read or write,
and Fairfax was so smart. The teacher in our school
wanted Fairfax to study to be a minister or a doctor,
but he never would. He said he thought the more
colored people try to raise themselves, the worse
they get treated. He felt so bad, always, about the
way colored people were treated. He said white
folks wanted them to be low-down, so he was going
to be. I used to tell him how wrong this was, and
how the good white people weren't like that, but he
didn't have any patience. Colored people have got
to have patience. Our mother was always patient.
And my husband and I manage pretty well. But
Fairfax was proud. And colored people can't be
proud. I don't believe he ever let you-all know how
he liked the way the folks up your way treated him.
He said their folks taught the white children to call
him mister just like a white man, and that the white

people used to ask him to parties and dances. He tried to go, he said, but at the door, he'd remember all the times when white people made a scene and called him a nigger and got mad if he even stood near them on the street, and looked at him that way white people do. . . . if you were colored you'd know what I mean. And then he just didn't dare risk it. When he was a boy and something like that happened, it used to make him down sick so he couldn't eat for days. And when he got up to where you live, it was too late. My husband and I had Fairfax taken to our old home town in Virginia and buried there beside our mother."

The air-raid was over when I finished that letter. The noisy bombardment of hate and revenge was quiet. The night was as still there in France as in the graveyard in Virginia. I was very thankful to know that Fairfax was sleeping beside his mother.

We are back in Vermont now, the curtain lowered over air-raids and barrages. Everything goes on as before.

The other evening we were all down at the schoolhouse for an entertainment. The children spoke pieces, and then we had a dance. About eleven o'clock some of us went out to the entry-room and began to serve the ice-cream. One of my neighbors said, after a while, "Do you remember how Fairfax used to get all dressed up so nice, and then always stayed around outside to watch?"

"Yes," I remembered.

"Sometimes," said another one of the women, "sometimes when we're out here like this, it seems to me when I look up quick and glance out there in the dark, as though I could almost see him there now."

After a time, some one else said, " 'Twas a pity he never would come in."

PROFESSOR PAUL MEYER

"MASTER of the Word." I never could remember where I had read that phrase—perhaps as a child in an old story-book about enchanters; but I knew whom it described when I first saw Professor Meyer speaking to his class in the Ecole des Chartes. Not in any metaphorical sense, but in the plain literal meaning of the phrase, was he Master of the Word. He made the title "Philologist" put on purple and gold.

The sallow young seminarists in their scant black gowns, keen, pale, young students who had come from Russia, Italy, Roumania, and Finland, sat motionless and intent, their eyes fixed on him unwaveringly for the two long hours of these daily lectures. Words were the living creatures in that room. They were born before our eyes in the remote childhood of the race, and swept down through the ages till there they were in our own language, issuing every day from our own lips, an ironic reminder that all the days of our lives were no more than an hour in the existence of those disembodied and deathless sounds.

From his youth the vigorous old man had transferred all his life to the world of words—and had
found it an enchanted kingdom, something sure and
lasting in the quicksands of human existence. From
inside the walls of his safe refuge he watched the
world outside suffer and despair and cry out and
die. And he marveled at its folly. He himself knew
none of these fitful moods. He was always of a
steady, kind, and humorous cheerfulness, and always the most compelling of talkers. No impassioned orator declaiming on an emotional theme could
hold more breathlessly attentive his listeners than
this tall, stooping, plain old Jew, when in his rapid
conversational staccato he traced out the life of a
word, told the Odyssey of its wanderings in the
mouths of men, so much less able to withstand death
and time than this mere breath from out their
mouths. He did this not with the straining effort of
the orator, but as naturally as he breathed or
thought. His mind was constantly revolving such
cycles, and when he spoke he was but thinking
aloud, always with the same zest, day after day, always alert, with never a flagging of interest, with
never a moment of treacherous wonder about the
value of anything. I knew him when I was passing
through one of those passions of doubt which mark

one's entry into adult life, and I never could be done with marveling at him. I was grateful to him, too, for he showed the most amused sympathetic kindliness to the foreign girl, groping her way forward.

I think he was sorry for me, for any one tempted to step into human and prosaic life. He stood at the door of his ordered, settled, established life, and called to me to construct one like it, to do as he had done, to turn away from the sordid comedy of personality, and step into the blessed country of impersonal intellectual activity. Many things turned me toward his path: the great weight of his mature personality (he was over seventy then and I was twenty), my immense admiration for his learning, my interest in his subject, my intuitive dread of the guessed-at strain of human emotions. You must not think that his world was austere or rarefied. He had found there, with no penalties to pay, all the amusement, the drama, the struggle, the rewards, the entertainment, which men find in the human world, and pay for so dearly. He never knew a bored or listless moment in his life, nor did any one in his company.

Every Tuesday and Thursday, after that two-hour lecture to the seminarists, there was a half hour intermission before the next class—eight or ten advanced students—met in his oak-paneled, half-basement office, rich with precious books, to discuss with him a curious Old-French manuscript which he had discovered in the library at Cassel.

I have never in my life known anything more sparkling and stimulating than those half-hour intermissions. The old man always clapped on his hat, talking incessantly as usual, and, stretching his long legs to a stride which kept me trotting like a little dog at his side, started up the Boulevard St. Michel towards the Odéon, to the pastry-shop which calls itself "of the Medicis." As soon as his tall form showed in the distance, and the inimitable, high, never-to-be-forgotten squeak of his voice could be heard, one of the elegant young-lady waitresses bestirred herself—for the pastry-shop was proud of its famous patron. She always had *babas au rhum* waiting for us, as this was the only pastry Professor Meyer considered worth eating. I do not like *babas au rhum* myself, but who was I to set up my insignificant opinion against so great a man? So I ate the wet sop docilely, considering it a small price to pay for the stories that went with it, stories that blew the walls away from around us, and spread there the rich darkness of the Middle Ages. There were

stories out of medieval manuscripts as yet unattri-
buted and unedited, heaped in the upper rooms of
the Ambrosiana at Milan, of the untold riches, unclassified and unarranged of the Bodleian, which
Paul Meyer described with apostolic fervor; of
priceless scripts discovered in impossible places, by
incredible coincidences; of years of fruitless work
on an obscure passage in the Grail-cycle, suddenly
cleared up because a Greek priest in Siberia had
discovered a manuscript bound in with an old Bible.

Or if he were in a playful mood, the mood the
waitresses adored and hoped for, he would begin
juggling with the names of things about us, the trim
shoes on their feet, the brooches at their throats, the
ribbon in their well-kept hair; and with a pyrotech-
nic display of laughing erudition, would hunt those
words around and around through all the languages
where they had tarried for a time, back through history—the Renaissance, the Middle Ages, the Dark
Ages, Late Latin, the Empire—till they ended in the
long-drawn sonorous Sanscrit chant of an early
Aryan dialect, which Professor Meyer rendered
with a total disregard of onlookers.

After one of these flights, we came to ourselves
with a start, looking around with astonishment at
our everyday dress and surroundings and bodies.

Or perhaps it was a story out of his life, his long, long life, of which not a day had been lost from his work. My favorites, I remember, were the Tarascon stories. Ages and ages ago, when Paul Meyer was a very young man, one of the brilliant pioneers in the study of Old French, the municipal authorities of Tarascon employed him to come and decipher the Town records, faithfully kept from the beginning of time, but in their strange medieval scripts, with the abbreviations, conventional signs, and hand-writings of the past centuries, wholly unintelligible to the modern Tarasconians. The young savant spent a whole winter there, studying and copying out these manuscripts, a first experience of the in-tense, bright pleasure such work was to give him all his life long. The quick-hearted southerners in the town, loving change and novelty, delighted to see the young, new face among them, welcomed him with meridional hospitality, and filled his leisure hours with the noisy, boisterous fun of Provence. He made friends there whom he never forgot, and every year after that he made the long trip to Tarascon to have a reunion with those comrades of his youth. But he lived long, much longer than the quickly-consumed southerners, and one by one, the friends of Tarascon were absent from the annual reunion.

They were fewer and fewer, older and older, those men used up by the fever of living, and they fell away from the side of the vigorous man who had chosen for his own the unchanging world of the intellect. "And finally, last year," said Professor Meyer on one occasion, "when I went back, they were all gone. Every one! I had to go to the cemetery to have a visit with them."

As I gazed at him, astounded by the unbroken matter-of-factness of his tone, no self-pity in it, he went on, his voice brightening into enthusiasm, "So I went and had another look at the town records. Such a glorious collection of scripts. Not one known style missing!"

He regretted deeply the death of the much-loved Gaston Paris, his great colleague at the Collège de France, whose name was always linked with his in the glory of the renaissance of Old-French studies, but his lamentations were over the work unfinished, the priceless manuscripts yet unedited. When the news came of the tragic family disgrace of one of the greatest of German editors of Old-French texts, Paul Meyer was moved almost to tears. They were not of sympathy with the sorrow of the other scholar, but of exasperation that any man, especially one filled with irreplaceable knowledge of his subject, could let so ephemeral a thing as human relations distract him from the rich fields to be tilled in the kingdom of words.

During the second trial of Dreyfus, Paul Meyer was called to testify as a handwriting expert and gave his testimony in favor of Dreyfus, the evidence, he said, being unmistakable. It was at the height of the Dreyfus re-trial, when all France was throbbing with hate and suspicion like an ulcer throbbing with fever. Professor Meyer was abominably treated by the opposition, attacked in the streets, insulted, boycotted, his classes filled with jeering young men who yelled him down when he tried to speak. His bearing through this trial is one of the momentous impressions of my life. He did not resent it, he made no effort to resist it, he struck no melodramatic attitude, as did many of the fine men then fighting for justice in France. He smothered the flame out, down to the last spark by his total disregard of it. What did he care for howling fanatics in one camp or another? Nothing! He had been asked to pass judgment on a piece of handwriting and he had done it. There was nothing more to be said.

I cannot forget the slightest shade of his expression as he stood one day, on the platform of his

classroom, chalk in hand, ready to write out an out-
line on the blackboard, waiting, while the yelling
crowd of *"manifestants,"* mostly young men in flowing black neckties, with straggling attempts at
beards on their pimply faces, stamped and hooted
and shrieked out, "Dirty Jew! What were you
paid? Shut up! Shut up! What was your price,
dirty Jew?" and other things less printable. And
yet, although I can shut my eyes now and see that
harsh, big-nosed, deeply-lined old face, with the
small, bright eyes under the bristling white eyebrows, I can not think of any words to describe its
expression—not scornful, not actively courageous,
not resentful, not defiant; rather the quiet, unex-
cited, waiting look of a man in ordinary talk who
waits to go on with what he has to say until a pounding truck of iron rails has time to pass the windows.
He stood looking at his assailants, the chalk ready
in his bony fingers, and from him emanated so profound a sense of their entire unimportance, of the
utterly ephemeral quality of their emotion compared
to the life of the consonant he was about to discuss,
that little by little they were silenced. Their furious voices flattened out to an occasional scream
which sounded foolish even to their own ears. They
looked at each other, got up in a disorderly body

and stamped out of the room. The last one might have heard Professor Meyer's high, squeaky voice stating, "Thus in Picardy and in the north of Normandy, Latin *C* before *a* did not undergo the change noted in other provinces, and we still find it pronounced. . . ."

The pale, keen seminarists in their long, black gowns, and the American girl, whipped out their notebooks and were at once caught up into the Paul-Meyer world where no storms blew.

When, three or four years after the beginning of this friendship—it was not precisely that, but I cannot think of another name to call it—I made my final choice and stepped out of his safe, windless realm into human life, it was with some apprehension that I went to tell him that I was engaged to be married and would study Philology no more. I might have known better than to be apprehensive. What did he care? What was one more or less among the disciples of Philology, as long as the words were there? Also, he laughingly refused to consider my decision as final. He seemed to stand at the door of Philology, calling after me with perfect good humor, as I walked away, "When you're tired of all that, come back. I'm always here."

In the years after this, whenever we passed through Paris I went to see him, stepping back into my girlhood as I stepped over the threshold of the Ecole des Chartes. Professor Meyer was very old now, but showed not the slightest sign of weakness or infirmity. One evening when I went hurriedly to say good-by before we sailed for home, I found him in his study, in that rich, half-basement room, lined with books. The green-shaded lamp burned clear and steady as though there were no wind in the world to shake a flame. The gray, plain, old man looked up from the yellow parchment he was deciphering, and in a sudden gust I had a new revelation of the insatiability of the human heart. I was a complete, fulfilled, vigorous woman, a happy wife, a writer beginning to feel an intoxicating interest in creative work, joyously awaiting the birth of my first child; but I knew for an instant there, the bitterest envy of the lot of the old scholar, half buried though he was in the earth, safe in the infinite security of his active brain.

The last time I saw him was two years later. We had been in Italy and were to pass through Paris on the way home. My little daughter was eighteen months old, a mere baby still, and I wrote Professor Meyer to ask him if he could not for once reverse the usual procedure and come to see me. He answered, setting a day, and informing me that he had been and still was very ill. "I will give you details when I see you."

When he came into the room I was shocked at his appearance, and horrified when he told me what had happened to him. He had been as usual in the summer, at Oxford, delving in the unclassified treasures of the Bodleian, and had started home. The Channel steamer arrived late at night at Boulogne, and he had chosen to sleep there, instead of taking the night train to Paris.

He had gone to sleep apparently in his usual health, but when he woke up in the morning he had lost his control of words. He could not bring them into the simplest order. He could not command a single one to his use. He could not say who he was, nor where he wanted to go, although he knew these facts perfectly. The moment he tried to speak, there swooped down between him and his meaning, a darkening throng of words. All the words in the world were there, Greek, Sanscrit, Provençal, Italian, Old-French, tearing furiously through his mind. But not the simple words in his own language to say that he was Professor Paul Meyer of the Ecole des Chartes, who wanted to buy a ticket to Paris. He stood there, helpless, facing the staring chamber-maids, cut off from them, from every one by this wild, invisible storm. They thought him an idiot, escaped from his friends, and ran away from him. As he told me about it, he looked sick and gray, and the sweat stood out on his forehead.

It had lasted for three days. For three days and three nights he had felt himself drowning in words, words that flooded up about him so that he was fighting for air. Never for an instant was he able to take his attention from their crazy flight through his mind, and never able to stop one long enough to use it. He suffered, suffered more than he had thought any human being could and retain consciousness, had after the first day fallen into a high fever, so that they feared for his life. Hour after hour he had lain on his bed, helpless, trying with all his strength to fight away those words long enough to remember what he wished to say.

And then, on the morning of the fourth day, click! Something snapped into place inside his mind, and there he was, very worn, very weak, but perfectly himself again, Professor Paul Meyer of the Ecole des Chartes. He had reached home safely, though strengthless and exhausted, and the next morning had wakened again to that horror. It had lasted an hour then, but it had come twice since—once as he was lecturing before his class!

He never knew when it might be upon him. As he opened his mouth to speak at any moment, he could not be sure that words would not burst from his command again. Even as he told me this, he glanced at my baby daughter, whom I had brought out to show him. For an instant his face whitened in so terrible a glare of panic that I screamed and clutched his arm. It was over. He was drawing a long breath and wiping his shaking lips with his handkerchief. "For an instant as I looked at her I could not think of the word 'baby,'" he said pitifully. "It was there, waiting to come on me again."

It seemed to me that he was not fit to go about the streets alone, and when he started to go away I asked him if he would not like to have me take him home. He hung his proud old head and said nothing. I went to get my hat and as no one happened to be at home with whom to leave the baby, I took her on my arm.

We went silently through the familiar Paris streets, the stooping old man towering on one side of me, the rosy baby heavy on my shoulder. When we reached his door, his concierge saw us and came out to meet us, nodding knowingly to me, and behind his back, tapping her forehead. I took his great bony old hand for a last clasp and said good-by. He went away up the stairs led by the concierge.

Three months after this I read in a newspaper a cabled notice of the death of the distinguished scholar, M. Paul Meyer, founder and for many years head of the Ecole des Chartes. He died, so the notice said, "from an obscure form of aphasia."

"WHILE ALL THE GODS . . ."

*"While all the gods Olympus' summit crowned,
Looking from high to see the wondrous sight."*
                                      ILIAD, XXII.

I WAS spading up the earth in the dahlia-bed, when
the children came up, a shouting band of them, just
out of school, and noticed that the angleworms
were "out." This first, indubitable sign of spring in
Vermont always suggests to adolescent Vermonters
the first fishing expedition. But ten-year-olds and
under think of the early brood of first-hatched
chicks.

"Hey, Jimmy, *angleworms!*"

"Carl, run get a can!"

"Here's a fat one!"

They swooped down on me and squatted along the
edge of the spaded earth, pecking and snatching and
chattering like a flock of sparrows. As I spaded
on, I heard bits of their talk, "Won't the chicks just
love them!" "First worms *those* chicks ever saw."
"No, Carl, that's too few, let's wait till we get a lot.
It's such fun to drop in a whole bunch." "They *love*
angleworms so!"

Then I heard the inevitable fanciful suggestion from the imaginative one of the group, "I bet we seem to the chicks just like giants . . . no, giants are always mean . . . like gods."

They fell on this idea, chattering and snatching, as they had at the worms: "*Let's* be gods! I'll be Jupiter."

"I want to be Mars."

"Loki! Loki!"

"I want to be Thor!"

"No, *I* want to be Thor!"

"I was just going to be Thor, myself!"

Everybody wanted to be Thor, it seemed. They trooped off to the poultry-yard, still disputing the question.

When I passed the brooder-house a little later, a group of exasperated gods hung over the low wire-netting, gesticulating and crying out on the idiocy of chicks. They fell on me for sympathy, and from their babbling account I made out that the chicks had acted just as chicks always act and always have acted from the beginning of time.

The gods had proudly put down in the midst of the little world of their beneficiaries the mass of angleworm wealth which they had gathered with such good intentions of giving pleasure.

"All they had to do was to pitch right in and enjoy themselves," cried Jupiter, wrathfully.

And what had they done? Well, first of all they had been afraid, running to look at the squirming heap of treasure, peeping shrilly in agitation, and running frantically away with fluttering wings and hearts.

The circle of omnipotents, hanging over the wire-netting had been able to endure this foolishness with an approach to the necessary god-like toleration of the limitations of a lesser race. One of the Thors, it seemed, the six-year-old-one, had tried to hurry up the progress of the race, by catching one of his pin-headed charges and holding him firmly in a benevolent small hand, directly in front of the delicious food, "where he couldn't *help* seeing how good it was, seems 's if," explained Thor Number Three, to me.

But the chick had, it appeared, been perfectly capable of not seeing how good it was, because his mind was entirely taken up with his terror at being held. He had merely emitted one frenzied screech of horror after another till the other chicks began to run about and screech too, and the older, more experienced gods had sharply told young Thor that he didn't know so much about this god-business as he thought he did, and that experience had told them the only thing to do was to let the chicks alone till they got used to a new idea. That always took forever, they informed their young colleague.

So after this they had waited and waited and *waited,* while the chicks fluttered, and peeped and ran away from what they really wanted above everything; from what the gods had so kindly put there for them to enjoy.

"Gee *whiz!*" said Mars disdainfully. "Wouldn't you think they'd know enough for *that!* There was room for every last one of them to stand around the pile, and eat all they wanted, without stirring a toe."

Finally, one bold adventurer had struck his beak experimentally into the pile, pulled out a tasty piece of meat, and turned aside to gobble it down.

And *then* what?

Did the other chicks follow his sensible example and begin at last to profit by their opportunity.

"No! no! no!" A chorus of all the gods assured me that nothing like that had happened. Instead, with shrill twitters of excitement, all the twenty or more chicks had thrown themselves on that one, to wrest his bit from him.

"Honest to goodness, they *did!*" Loki affirmed to

me, passionately, as if feeling that I could not possibly believe in such unreason if I had not seen it.

The chick with the worm had taken to his heels,
unable to swallow his prize because of the hunt
against him. Up and down the little world of their
yard, he had run frantically, wildly, and silently
(because of his mouth being full). And up and
down, wildly, frantically and vociferously (their
mouths being empty) his fellow-chicks had pursued
him, bent on catching him and taking away from
him whatever it was he prized enough to try to possess. As he turned and doubled to escape them,
they turned and doubled in a pack, slipping,
falling, and trampling on each other in their blind
fury.

Presently, "What do you *think!*" cried the oldest
of the Thors. "He got so rattled that he lost his piece
of worm out of his mouth, but the others didn't give
him time to tell them that. Anyhow, they'd yelled
and carried on so, they had him up in the air. He
didn't know by that time what he *was* doing; and he
kept on legging it as hard as ever, and they after
him."

By and by, this insane flight and agitation had
so exhausted them all that they were staggering
feebly on their tiny legs, and unable to emit more

than hoarse squawks as they ran. Then, apparently by chance, as he darted zigzag to and fro, he had run under a corner of the brooder. Instantly . . . ah-h-h, the grateful warmth and darkness had suggested rest to his weary soul; with a long murmured "che-e-eep" of utter relief, he had settled down against the wall of the brooder to close his eyes. And each of his pursuers, as they dashed in after him, had seized on the Heaven-sent opportunity for rest after the terrible tension of the struggle for existence, imposed on them by a cruel fate, and had with a sigh and a relieved, whispered twitter, given himself over to sleep and dreams.

At the time when I came up, every chick was sound asleep in the brooder, while outside in the middle of their world, lay the untouched pile of angleworms, bare and open to view under the bright spring sky.

"Can you beat it!" said Mars contemptuously.

He turned away from such unimaginable imbecility to a new idea, "Say, kids!" he bellowed, although they were all within touching distance of him, "lets be cops and robbers!"

They flared up like tinder to a spark, "All right! I'll be Chief of Police!"

"I'll be a detective!"

"I'll be the robber captain . . . cave's under the hay, as usual."

"No, *I* wanted to be robber captain!"

"No, me, me!"

They all wanted to be robber captain, it seemed. They streamed away to the barn, wrangling over this.

All but one. The youngest Thor, newer than the others to the god-business, still hung over the wire-netting, grieving, "Seems 's if . . . if we could only *tell* them! They *love* angleworms so!" he said pity-ingly. "If I could only think of some way to *teach* them how to stand around quietly, and each one get all he wanted to. They'd have such a *good* time!" he yearned over them.

As I said nothing, he asked of the world in general, "Why won't they? Oh, why *won't* they?"

I let fall insidiously, "I wonder how the angle-worms like it?" The little god stared at me with startled eyes; and then at the worms. He looked at them as though he saw them for the first time. His tender young face was fairly vacant with his surprise before a new idea.

Then he began slowly to climb over the wire-netting.

When I went back to the dahlia-bed, he was carefully burying the angleworms again.

His young face wore an expression of puzzled bewilderment.

SCYLLA AND CHARYBDIS

WHEN the elders of our family could think of nothing else to worry about they put in their time to good advantage on little Cousin Maria Pearl Manley. Yes—Maria Pearl—that was really the poor child's name, given in baptism. You can see that her troubles began early. That name was symbolical of what her life was to be, sharply divided between her mother's family (they were the ones who insisted on the Maria) and her father's folks, who stood out for the Pearl. Her father had died before she was born, and her mother lived only a few months after the baby came, and was so mortally ill that no one thought of naming the poor little girl. It was after her mother's death, when the two hostile families could collect themselves, that the long struggle over the child began by giving her that name.

Thereafter she was Maria for six months of the year, the period when she stayed with the Purdons; and Pearl the other half-year, when she was with her father's family, the Manleys. "The poor little tyke, not even a fixed name of her own," my grand-mother used to say, pitying the child's half-yearly oscillations between those two utterly dissimilar houses "where there's nothing the way it should be in either one!" The circle of compassionate elders used to continue, "Dear, dear! What can the poor little thing ever learn, with such awful examples always before her eyes."

As I look back now, I must admit that such severe characterizations were really not due to the natural tendency of all elders to be sure that children are being badly brought up. Those two houses which formed the horizon of Maria Pearl's life were certainly extravagant examples of how not to conduct life. The Purdon grandfather and grandmother and aunt were the strictest kind of church people (the kind who make you want to throw a brick through the church-windows), narrow, self-righteous, Old-Testament folks, who dragged little Maria (the "Pearl" was never pronounced inside their doors) to Church and Sunday-School and prayer-meeting and revivals and missionary meetings, and made her save all her pennies for the heathen. Not that she had very many to save, for the Purdons, although very well-to-do, were stingier than any other family in town. They loved money, it tore at the very fibers of their being to part with it, and they avoided this mental anguish with considerable skill. Although their competent "management" allowed them to live comfortably, there were few occasions which brought them to the point of letting any actual cash out of their hands. The dark, plain, well-fitting garments which clothed little Maria were never bought, but made over out of her grandmother's clothes; the soap which kept her clothes immaculately clean had cost no money, but was part of the amazing household economies in which old Mrs. Purdon was expert and into which she introduced Maria with conscientious care. The child learned to darn and patch and how to make soap out of left-over bits of fat, and how to use the apple-culls for jelly and how, year after year, to retrim last season's hat for this.

From morning till night she lived in a close, airless round of intensive housekeeping and thrift. She spread newspapers down over the rugs, so the sun should not fade them; she dried every scrap of orange peel to use as kindling, she saved the dried beef jars to use for jams, she picked berries all day long instead of playing, and then sat up late with Aunt Maria and Grandmother, picking them over and canning them, on the stove in the woodshed, to avoid litter in the kitchen. She always wore gingham aprons, even to school, which no other children did, and she was treated as though she had offended against the Holy Ghost, if she forgot to wash her rubbers and put them in their place in the closet under the stairs. She was rigorously held to a perfect performance of her share of the housework, making up her bed with the fear of the Lord in her poor little heart lest the corners be not square enough, poking desperately at the corner of the windows she washed and polished, and running her finger anxiously over the dishes she wiped to be sure they had that glass-smooth surface which only repeated rinsings in very hot water can give. Then when all was done, her reward was to take her seat in their appallingly neat sitting-room and, to the accompaniment of Aunt Maria's reading aloud out of a church paper, to set tiny stitches in the stout, unbleached cotton of which her underwear was made. They were really dreadful, the six months she passed with her mother's people.

But the other half-year was scarcely better, although she might have journeyed to another planet with less change in her surroundings. When the day came, the first of January, for her departure from the Purdon household, her solidly-constructed little trunk was filled with her solidly-constructed little clothes, her hair was once more rebraided to an even harder finish, her face was once more polished with the harsh, home-made soap, and her nails were cut to the quick. "It's the *last* time the poor child will have any decent care, till she comes back," Grandmother Purdon would say bitterly, buttoning up with exactitude the stout, plain warm little coat, and pulling down over Maria's ears the firmly knit toque of dark-blue wool. They all went down to the station to make sure she took the right train, and put her, each of them separately, in the hands of the Conductor. They kissed her good-by, all but Grandfather, who shook hands with her hard. It was at that moment that Maria's frozen little heart felt a faint warmth from the great protecting affection they had for her, which underlay the rigor of their training and which they hid with such tragic completeness.

The first day of the arrival at the Manley's was always a dream of delight! To emerge from the silent rigidity of the Purdon house into the cheerful, easy-going, affectionate noise of the Manley home, to exchange the grim looks of Grandmother Purdon for the exuberant caresses of Grandmother Manley; to leave behind all stringent admonitions to put your wraps on a certain hook, and to be allowed to fling them down on the floor where you stood. . . . Little Pearl (she was never called Maria by the Manleys) felt herself rebounding into all the sunshine and good-nature, as a rubber ball rebounds from a hard stone wall. She flung herself around Aunt Pearl's neck, and paid back with interest the "forty thousand kisses" which were the tradition in that home. She flung herself into play with the innumerable little cousins, who cluttered up the floor; for there was always a married aunt or two back home, with her family, while an invisible uncle-by-marriage tried somewhere in a vague distance, to get a hypothetical job. She flung herself into her bed at night joyfully reveling in the fact that its corners were not turned squarely, and that the pillow-case had last seen the wash-tub on about the same date that Aunt Carry's husband had last had a job. It was a care-free dream to go to bed whenever she pleased—eleven o'clock if that suited her taste—with nobody to tell her to wash, or to brush her teeth, or comb her hair; and to lie there watching Aunt Carry and Aunt Pearl, who always sat up till midnight at least, putting their hair in curl-papers and talking about the way the neighbor next door treated his wife. This was life!

But already the very next morning the dream was not quite so iridescent, as with no one to wake her, she opened her eyes at twenty minutes of nine, and knew that she had to be at school at nine! She sprang up, shivering in the cold room (Grandfather Manley never could manage the furnace, and also there were periods when there was mighty little money to buy coal) and started to claw herself into her clothes. But always just at first she forgot the Manley ways, and neglected to collect everything she had taken off, and put it under her pillow, the only spot in which you could keep things for yourself in that comfortably communistic family. Her shoes were gone, her nice new calf-skin school shoes. She went flying out, comb in hand, tearing at the tangles in her hair, as she went, asking if anybody had seen her shoes. Aunt Carry, still in her nightgown, with a smeary baby in her arms, said, yes, she'd let her Elmer have them to run down to the grocery store to get some bread. Somehow they'd got out of bread and poor Aunt Pearl had had to go off to her work with only some crackers to eat. Surely little Pearl didn't grudge the loan of her shoes to her cousin. The bread was for all of them, and Elmer couldn't find his shoes, and anyhow one of them had a big hole in it and the snow was deep.

"But, Aunt Carry, how can I get to school? I'll be late!"

"Well, gracious, what if you are! Don't be so fussy! Time was made for slaves!" That was Aunt Carry's favorite motto, which she was always citing, and for citing which there were plenty of occasions in her life. Little Pearl thought somewhat resentfully, as she rummaged in her trunk for her other shoes, that if Aunt Carry had to enter the school-room late and get scolded, she'd think differently about time! But anyhow it was fun to wear her best shoes if she liked, and to watch their patent leather tips twinkling as she scurried about. They twinkled very fast during that quarter of an hour, as Pearl collected her wraps (her mittens she never did find after that day) and tried to scare up something for breakfast in the disordered kitchen, where the cat, installed on the table, was methodically getting a breakfast by licking the dirty plates clean. Pearl was not so lucky, and had to go off to school with a cracker in one hand and a piece of marshmallow cake in the other. The less said about her hair the better! Grandmother Manley's "forty thousand kisses" were not quite so wonderful this morning as they had been last night.

At noon Pearl ran home, her stomach in her heels,

all one voracious demand for good food. Aunt
Carry was crocheting by the window and there was
no sign of any lunch. "Mercy me!" cried Grandmother Manley, "Is it noon? Why, how the morning has gone!" And then with the utmost compunc-
tion they both rushed out into the kitchen and began to hurry with all their might to get something
for Pearl to eat. The kitchen fire was pretty low,
and there were no potatoes cooked, and Aunt Carry
had forgotten to order any eggs, and the milk bottle
had been left outside and was frozen hard. Hurry
as they might and apologize to Pearl almost with
tears as they did, it was very little that Pearl had
eaten when she went back to school, and she knew
well enough that they would forget tomorrow, just
as they had to-day. No, already Pearl felt that life
could not be made *wholly* out of kisses and good
nature. By nightfall, her thin kid shoes were rather
scuffed and very wet, with a break in one of the
patent leather tips where Cousin Tom had stepped
on it, in a scuffle with his brother. Little Pearl
nursed her sore toe and broken shoe with a weary
feeling.

Always at the end of the six months with the
Manleys, Pearl was nearly a nervous wreck. She
was behind in her lessons, since there was not a quiet

spot in the house to study, and even if there had been you couldn't escape from the noise of the trombone, which Aunt Carry's oldest was learning to play; she was underweight and anæmic for lack of regular food and enough sleep . . . it wasn't much use to go to bed when nobody else did, and Aunt Pearl and Aunt Carry always visited in more than audible voices as they put up their hair in curlers; she had nothing to wear (since nothing had been renewed or mended) except a blue silk dress which Grandfather Manley had bought for her in a fit of affection, and some mostly-lace underwear which Aunt Carry had sat up till all hours making for her, so that "she should have something pretty like the other girls!" But for an active little girl, mostly-lace underwear soon was reduced to the quality of mosquito netting; and a blue silk dress in the Manley's house was first cousin to Sir Walter Raleigh's cloak in the mud-puddle.

With all the family she had been night after night to the moving pictures and not infrequently was kept up afterwards by the hysterics of little Nelly, Aunt Carry's nervous, high-strung five-year-old, who saw men with revolvers pointed at her, and desperadoes about to bind and gag her, till Pearl more than half saw them too, and dreamed of them after-

wards. She had suffered the terrible humiliation of
having the teacher send her home with a note saying that her hair must be washed and kept in better
order, a humiliation scarcely lessened by the outraged affection of the Manleys, who had taken her
into their loving arms, to moan over their darling's
hurt feelings. She had thereafter made frantic efforts to keep her own hair in order, with what brush
and comb she could salvage out of the jetsam in the
room which was at once hers and the aunts' bedroom; but if she complained that her hair-ribbons
disappeared, or were crumpled in a corner of the
drawer, she was told comfortably, not to be fussy,
"For goodness' sakes, don't make such a fuss
about things! Folks that do never have a minute's
comfort in life, nor nobody else in the house
either."

Yes, it was a rather pale, wild-eyed little Pearl,
who on the first day of July scrambled together
into her trunk what she could find, put on the hat
which had been so bright and pretty when Aunt
Pearl gave it to her at Easter, and which now after
two months with the Manleys looked like a floor-
cloth. She did not put her hands over her ears to
deaden a little the volume of noise as they all
crowded about her in the station to say their affec-

tionate and vociferous good-byes, but that was only because she did not want to hurt their feelings. The instant she was in the train, she always hid her face in her arms, quivering all over with nervous tension. Oh, the noise the Manleys always made over everything, and the confusion they were always in, when they tried to do anything, colliding with each other, and dropping things, and squealing and screaming! And it was all right for them to be warm-hearted and generous—but when they slathered money on ice-cream, and then didn't have enough to pay for her ticket, till they'd borrowed it . . . !

Well, then there was the re-entrance into the Purdon house, the beautiful, fragrant cleanliness of everything, the dustless order, her own room, with the clean, white sheets, and her own safe closet into which nobody would ever plunge rummaging. And Aunt Maria so quiet and calm, with her nice low voice, and Grandmother Purdon so neat with her white lace collar, and her lovely white hair so well-brushed, and oh, the good things to eat. . . . To sit down to a well-ordered table, with a well-cooked savory mutton stew, and potatoes neither watery nor underdone, and clear apple jelly quivering in a glass dish! And the clean, clean dishes! Had Maria ever complained of having to rinse the dishes too often!

She remembered the dried-on bits of food always to be felt on the Manley plates . . . !

The first evening too was always dream-like, the quiet, deft despatching of the dishes, in the kitchen shining with cleanliness, and then all the evening free, and so quiet, so blessedly quiet, with no trombone, and no whoops of chatter or boisterous crying and laughing; no piano banging (except perhaps Aunt Maria softly playing a hymn or two) no children overturning chairs and slamming doors, no one falling up or downstairs, no crash of breaking crockery from the kitchen . . . little Maria sat on the well-swept porch behind the well-trained vines and soaked herself in the peace and quiet.

But by the next morning, the shine was a little off. When Aunt Maria came to wake her at half past six, *half past six* . . . why, no one at Grandfather Manley's thought of stirring till eight! And she was expected to wash and dress . . . not a button unbuttoned or a hair out of place under penalty of a long lecture on neatness . . . and "do" her room, even to wiping off the woodwork; and make her bed. Heavens! How fussy they were about those old corners! All this before she had a bit of breakfast. Then, breakfast with everybody's whole soul fixed on the work to be done, and nobody so much as dimly aware that it was a glorious, sunny, windy, summer day outside. Maria's heart sank, sank, sank, as she drank her perfectly made chocolate, and ate her golden-brown toast, till it struck the dismal level where it usually lived during the Purdon half-year. "Come, Maria, don't loiter over your food. The only way to get the work done is to go right at it!"

"Oh, Maria, do you call that folding your napkin? I call it crumpling it into a ball."

"You forgot to put your chair back against the wall, Maria. If we each do faithfully our share of what is to be done, it will be easier for us all."

"No, the *spoons* go there . . . mercy, no! not the forks!"

"Don't twitch the curtain so as you go by. It takes all the fresh out of it. I only ironed them yesterday."

"Why, Maria, whistling! Like a little street boy!"

The July sun might shine and the wind blow outside, inside the house it was always gray, windless November weather. She felt herself curl up like a little autumn leaf, and, with a dry rattle, blow about the rooms before the chill admonitory breath of Grandmother Purdon and Aunt Maria.

Yes, the family elders were right in pitying her, as a child brought up just as badly as it was possible to be; and nobody was surprised or blamed her a bit, when she got out of both families as rapidly and as unceremoniously as she could, by making a very early marriage with an anonymous young man, somebody she had met at a high-school dance. He seemed just like any young man, from the glimpse of him, which was all the family had, before their marriage; but nobody knew a thing about his character or whether he would make a good husband. And, indeed, there was a big doubt in the family mind as to whether Maria Pearl would be any sort of wife or home-maker. How could she have learned anything about rational living, the poor little tyke, hustled from one bad example to another through all the impressionable years of her life? Suppose she kept house like the Manleys! Horrors! Or suppose she took after the Purdons! Her poor husband!

. . . .

Nothing of the sort! There's not a happier home anywhere in the country than hers, nor a better housekeeper, nor a wiser mother. It's a perfect treat to visit in her cheerful, sunny, orderly house, or to talk with her well-brought-up, jolly children, or to see her well-fed, satisfied husband. And she herself is a joy to the eye, stout and rosy and calm. She is neither fussy nor slack, neither stingy nor extravagant, neither cold and repressed, nor slushy and sentimental.

How did it happen? Probably Maria Pearl doesn't know. But I do. And since it has happened, I can see perfectly how inevitable it was. Whenever the routine of her houskeeping begins to set too hard, and she feels like flying at muddy-footed, careless children with the acrimony natural to the good housekeeper, the memory of forlorn little Pearl among the Purdons softens and humanizes her words. And when the balance begins to swing the other way, when she tastes that first delicious, poisonous languour of letting things slide, when her Manley blood comes to the top, she has other memories to steady her. I have seen her sitting at the breakfast table, after the children are off to school, begin to sag in her chair, and reach with an indolent gesture for a tempting novel; and I knew what was in her mind as she sprang up with a start and began briskly to clear off the table and plan the lunch.

ART ATMOSPHERE

My cousin Angelica was one of the advance-guard. She bowed down and worshiped Whistler six months or so before the rest of humanity reached the adoration stage; and when she heard that he had opened a studio for "lady students" available to any one who would pay the entrance-fee—"just like one of the second-raters who teach at Carlorossi's"—she lost no time in making tracks for the Passage Stanislas, where, if I remember rightly, the Whistler studio was situated.

It was, just as rumor had said, like all other studio-classes of that sort, except that the fee was many times larger; but that was legitimate, Whistler being *the* thing that winter, and *the* thing always commanding a high price in the open market.

It was a large, grimly dirty, barn-like room, with a big sky-light towards the north. In it sat some twenty or thirty more-or-less-young ladies, most of them Americans (the fee was really *very* large) enveloped in voluminous, paint-stained aprons. They sat, as always in such studio-classes, in a circle around a platform, on which stood the model.

Once a week (or was it once a fortnight?) "the Master" drove up in a cab, made his way into the room amid palpable emanations of awe, and going from canvas to canvas shed upon the bowed head of each acolyte a little of the sacred fire of his genius.

My cousin Angelica, like the others, found this a more than satisfactory arrangement and considered that she received full value for her money. We heard little from her that winter but enthusiasm over the Whistler atmosphere and scorn of everything else. In any exhibition she was to be found in ecstasy before some barely visible human visage sunk in the gloom of a dusky corner at twilight, or a floating, whitish blur or two on a dark-blue canvas, which, she told us, represented the new artistic tradition, worth all the other artistic traditions produced since they carried the Cimabue Madonna through the streets—or was that a Giotto?

I was studying philology that year and had no quarrel with Angelica about that sort of thing. For all I cared, she could give her adherence to whichever artistic tradition took her fancy for the moment. But it was occasionally inconvenient to have her so slavishly tied to the studio-class on the days when they expected a criticism. Nothing could have tempted her away from one of those marvelous opportunities to profit by first-hand personal instruction from a first-rate living genius. Even when our one prosperous relative, Uncle Frederick, came through Paris and invited us over to the Right Bank to go to lunch with him at a fearfully expensive restaurant, and to sit in a fearfully expensive loge at the Français afterwards, Angelica had to go first to the studio.

I went with her, so that I could carry her off directly afterwards. This is what I saw and heard in the hour I spent there.

The day was a fine one of sunlight less tempered with gray than most Paris sunshine. The model was a stout, red-haired woman with the milk-white skin of red-haired people. From the great expanse of the skylight, there poured upon her opulent nude body, as smooth and white as a newly peeled almond, a flood of light that was sparkling, in spite of the north exposure. The room rang with the high, clear brightness of that white flesh in that morning light.

Around the model sat the thirty or so disciples of

the Master. While I waited for Angelica, I wandered around back of them, glancing at the canvases on their easels.

They had all painted the model the color of an old saddle. From one dim, cavernous sketch after another, a misty, smeary, dark-brown mass looked out waveringly from blue, or brown, or gray twilight. The red head glimmered faintly, attenuated by layers and layers of shadow. The disciples looked up at the gleaming white woman before them, reflecting the daylight as definitely as a sound tooth reflects it, and looked down happily and proudly on their dark, blurred canvases. You could see how pleased they were at the progress they were making. They had caught it, this time, they had caught what was the thing to catch.

"We'll have some fireworks, all right, when 'the Master' gets here," I thought to myself.

Presently he came. The door swung open, I caught a glimpse of the concierge performing the impossible in the way of holding the door open and effacing herself in one and the same gesture, and in came a dapper, immaculately dressed little old gentleman, with gray gloves and pearl-gray gaiters.

The disciples prostrated themselves, foreheads to the floor (or at least that is the impression they made on me in the first intense emotion of his entrance) and then stiffened to attention before their easels, not to miss a word of the down-dropping pearls and rubies.

The little old gentleman advanced with small, gentlemanly steps to the first of the easels, and contemplated the leather-brown South-Sea-Islander depicted on it. Every one of the students held her breath. So did I.

He looked at it a long time, his face imperturbable. Then with the traditional studio gesture I had seen all my life in studios—outstretched thumb, modeling in the air—he began saying what I had heard all my life in studios, "A little more shadow on the shoulder, I should say. And perhaps. . . . Yes, go into the modeling of that arm more deeply. On the whole very promising, very interesting."

He passed on to the next easel. One felt another devout heart turn over with a rustle. "Good! Well *felt*, that knee. But lacking in distinction, perhaps, the treatment of the hair. Go into the modeling of the hands more deeply."

He passed to the next. And the next. And the next. I heard a murmur of "Very promising . . . very interesting . . . deeper feeling about . . . keep it flat . . . subtle . . . relations of planes not quite . . . very promising . . . very interesting."

In half an hour it was over. He walked neatly back to the door, which the nearest student sprang to open, and with a courteous bow all around he disappeared, his face imperturbable to the last. If he lifted a cynical eyebrow in amusement, it was not till after the door had closed upon him.

Angelica and I were now free to go, and I proceeded to the difficult undertaking of cutting her out from the herd of art-students milling excitedly around and around before the canvases, "Did you hear what he said about my shoulder-blade?" "This was the plane he liked on my back." "He didn't object to the treatment of my . . ."

The model, however, showed an imperturbability as complete as that of the Master. Like him, she had earned her pay for a morning's work. As the door had closed on him, she had climbed down off the platform, and she was now calmly pulling her chemise on over her red head.

Angelica was still a little wild-eyed and emotional when we emerged on the street. "Isn't he *won*der-ful?" she said, clutching at my arm. "Can't you understand now what a privilege it is to . . ." She took ten minutes to blow off this high-pressure steam and come down to little wandering puffs like, "It *means* so much to have such precious contacts!" And, "You simply take it in through your *pores* when you are in the real art atmosphere."

Understand me, please, I do not venture to affirm that this is really all that took place. I am no art-student and never was. There may have been oceans more. But this is all that I saw.

COLONEL SHAYS

I DARE say when you studied American history you read about Shays' Rebellion, in Massachusetts, and duly learned that it was put down, and the instigators punished. But I am sure that you never knew, and never wondered, what became of Colonel Shays himself, of whom the history books say succinctly, "the leader himself, escaped."

I have never seen in print anything about the latter part of his life beyond one or two scanty and inaccurate references in one or two out-of-date books of reference; but all the older people in our town were brought up on stories about him, for it was to the valley just over the mountain from us that he fled after his last defeat. And later on, as an old man, he lived for some years in our town, in a house still standing, and told many people what I am going to set down here.

At the time when he made his escape from the officers of the State in Massachusetts, Vermont was, quaintly enough, an independent republic, all by itself, and hence a sufficient refuge for men fleeing from the officers of any State in the Union. Furthermore it was still rather wild, sparsely settled, none too respectful of any authority, and distinctly sympathetic to strangers who came from the east, south, or west over the mountains on the run, with the manner of men escaping from sheriffs. Sheriffs were not popular persons in Vermont in 1787.

But all this did not seem to make it a safe enough refuge to the man with a price set on his head, the man who had risked everything on the boldest of enterprises, and had lost everything. He passed by the rough scattered little hamlets and went into a remote, narrow, dark, high valley, which is to this day a place where a man might hide for years and never be seen. Colonel Shays, traveling at night, on foot, through the forests, came down into the Sandgate valley through the Beartown notch, over the mountains, and not a soul knew that he had come.

He made his first camp, which was also his permanent and last one, since he was never disturbed, high up on a shoulder of the mountain, overlooking the trail for a great distance, and densely surrounded with a thick growth of pine trees. Very cautiously, making no noise, using the ax and knife which were his only tools, he put up a rough shelter, and building a fire only at night in a hollow where rocks masked its flame, began cooking some of the game he caught. He lived in this way, all alone for years and years. Game was abundant; like most men of that time he was an adroit trapper, a good pioneer, and knew how to smoke and preserve the flesh of animals and to save their skins. For the first year he did not dare to let any one know that a man was living there, and literally saw not one soul.

Then one day about a year after he began this life, a little boy going fishing saw a tall, strong, black-haired stranger standing in the trail and holding a large packet of furs. He told the child to take the packet and ask his father for a bushel of seed-corn and a bag of salt. He specified that the man who brought it was to leave it just where they then stood and go away without waiting.

The child's father was a rough, half-civilized, good-natured trapper, who had had troubles of his own with unreasonable officers of the law in York State. When the child told his story, the father laughed knowingly, took the skins, got the seed-corn and the salt, left them in the place indicated, and kept a neighborly shut mouth. He could not read or write, had never heard of Shays' Rebellion, and supposed the man in hiding to be in the same situation as himself. Living as he did, it seemed no awful fate to make one's living out of the woods, and he thought little of the fact that he had a new neighbor.

After this, Colonel Shays began a little cultivation of the ground, in scattered places, hidden behind screens of thick trees, in a few natural clearings in the forest. He used to say that life was infinitely more tolerable to him after the addition to his diet of salt and cereals. After some months he risked a little more, and, buying them with furs worth forty times their value, he secured a few tools and some gunpowder. The transactions were always carried on through the child, the only one to see the fugitive.

Nothing has come down to me of what this terrible dead halt in mid-career, and this grim isolation from the world meant to the active, intelligent, ambitious man at the height of his powers. None of the old people who heard him talk seem to have asked him about this, or to have had any curiosity on the subject. Only the bare facts are known, that he lived thus for many years, till the little boy grew up, till his own hair turned gray and then white, till the few families in that valley were quite used to the knowledge that a queer, harmless old man was living up in the woods near the northern pass of the moun-

tains, miles from any neighbor. Once in a great
while, now, some one saw him—a boy fishing, a
hunter far on the trail of a deer, or a group of women
picking berries. He occasionally exchanged a few
words with his neighbors at such times, but he had
almost forgotten how to speak aloud. All the
stories about him mention the rough, deep, hoarse-
ness of his unused voice.

One day his nearest neighbor, meaning to do him
a kindness, told him with a rough good-will that he
might as well quit hiding now, "Whatever 'tis you
done, 'tis so long past now! And up here . . . nobody from your part of the country, wherever 'tis,
would ever be coming up here. And if they did they
wouldn't know you. Why, your own mother
wouldn't know you in them clothes, and with that
white beard."

It is said that Colonel Shays on hearing this, drew
back and looked down at himself with a strange air
of astonishment.

Apparently the advice stuck in his mind, for, some
weeks after this, he decided to risk it, and to make
the trip to Cambridge, the nearest town to those
mountain settlements. Early one morning the people of the Sandgate valley were astonished to see the
old man going down the trail of the valley which

led into the State road going to Cambridge. Well,
that was something to talk about! He was going
to town at last like anybody else.

Now, this happened a good many years after
Shays' Rebellion had failed, and the bitterness of
the feeling about it had died down. Although Colonel Shays could not know this, most people had even
forgotten all about him, and as for looking for him
to arrest him, nobody would have dreamed of doing
it. There were many other things in the world to
think of by that time and although to himself
Colonel Shays was still the dramatically hunted
fugitive with every man's hand against him, to other
people he had begun to sink into the history-book
paragraph, which he has since remained. His family
and friends in Massachusetts had waited till the occasion seemed favorable, and then petitioned for
his pardon, on the ground that he must be, if still
living, an old man now, quite harmless, and that it
would be only decent to let him come back to spend
his last days in his own home; and if he were dead,
his pardon would clear his family name, and
straighten out certain complications about his property. At first they had not succeeded. People still
remembered too vividly the treasonable attempt to

overturn the authority of the State, only just established and none too strong. But by and by, the pertinacity of the petitioners wore out the fading hostility to his name. He was proclaimed pardoned, and notices were sent to all American newspapers informing him that he could now return. This had happened a year before Colonel Shays had started down to Cambridge, but you may be sure that at that period no newspapers found their way to the Sandgate valley.

After a year had gone by, and no sign came from the fugitive, people generally thought him dead. But a fellow-townsman who had known him well by sight and who, some years after his flight, had married his youngest sister, volunteered to try to spread the news more widely than by newspaper. There had been a faint notion among his kinspeople that he had fled to Vermont, although they had taken care to keep this to themselves as long as he was an outlaw, and had now almost forgotten about it. Acting on this notion, Shays' brother-in-law took the long journey on horseback up into Vermont. He entered the state at Bennington and slowly worked his way north, branching off at every practicable road. But nowhere did he find any one who had ever heard of any such man as his wife's brother.

Colonel Shays had hidden himself only too well.

The Massachusetts man began to think his errand a futile one, and prepared to turn back. But on a chance he rode down to Cambridge, just over the New York line. Cambridge was the nearest town to a number of small valley settlements in Vermont. He would ask there if any one had seen or heard of the man he was seeking. He knew that men from the remote outlying settlements came to Cambridge to do their trading. He arrived rather late one evening and as he was no longer young, and very much tired by his long and fruitless journey, he slept that night in the Cambridge Inn.

For the rest of the story there are plenty of details, for Colonel Shays told over and over exactly what happened and just how he felt, and why he acted as he did. It seared deep into him, and to the end of his days, he always showed a consuming agitation in speaking of it.

He walked along the road, the first road he had seen since the night so many years ago when he had fled along the roads in Massachusetts. It seemed like iron to his buckskin-shod feet. He walked slowly for this and other reasons. Every house which came into view along the road brought him up short with a jerk like a frightened horse. The instinct to hide, to trust himself in no man's sight, had deformed his whole nature so that the bold leader of men halted, trembling and white-faced, at the sight of an ordinary farm-house. He forced himself to go on, to pass those sleeping homes, but after he had passed each one with his silent, stealthy wood-dweller's tread, he quickened his pace and looked fearfully over his shoulder, expecting to see men run out after him with warrants for his arrest.

By the time he approached Cambridge, the nervous strain was telling on him. He was wet with sweat, and as tired as though he had been four times over the mountains. Only a few people were abroad as it was the breakfast hour. Partly from the old fear of years, partly from the mere habit of total isolation, every strange face was startling to him. He felt his knees weak under him and sat down on a bench in front of the kitchen door of the Cambridge Inn to get his breath. He had been a man of powerful will and strong self-control or he never could have lived through those terrible years of being buried alive, and he now angrily told himself there was nothing to fear in this remote little hamlet, where everybody was used to the sight of men in buckskins coming down to trade their furs for gunpowder and salt. At the sight of all those human faces taking him back to the days of his human life, a deep yearning had come upon him to get back into the world of living men. He could have wept aloud and taken them into his arms like brothers. He was determined to master his tense nerves, to learn to move about among his fellow-men once more. In a moment, just a moment, he decided he would stand up and move casually over to the general store across the street where a lad was then unlocking the door. He would go in and make a purchase—the first in so many years!

He turned his head to glance into the kitchen of the Inn, and as he did so, the door opened, and a man came in, a traveler with a face familiar to him in spite of gray hair and wrinkles, a man he had known in Massachusetts, who knew him, and no friend of his, a man who had been on the other side in the Rebellion.

Colonel Shays' heart gave a staggering leap. He caught at the door-jamb and shrank out of sight. He heard the other voice say, "I stepped in to ask if any of you know whether Colonel Shays was ever heard of in this . . ."

And then the old man, running madly for his life, fled back to his den in the woods.

A whole decade passed after this, before he happened to learn in a conversation overheard between two trappers, that for eleven priceless, irreplaceable years, he had been a free man.

A GREAT LOVE

When my pretty young cousin and god-daughter, Flossie, fell in love with Peter Carr, we all felt rather apprehensive about her future. But Flossie faced the facts with an honest, even a rather grim resolution which surprised us. She said with only a little tremor in her voice that she never expected to occupy the place in Peter's heart which Eleanor Arling had taken forever, but that she loved him so much she was willing to take whatever he could give her. It wasn't *his* fault, she said, with the quaintest chivalric defiance of us, if poor Peter hadn't more to give. She thought a great love like that "was a noble thing in any one's life, even if it did make them perfectly miserable." If Miss Arling felt that personal happiness must be sacrificed for her art, why, that was an exalted attitude to take, and Peter's sorrow was "sacred in her eyes"; and so on and so forth—the usual things that are said in such cases by people who are in sympathy with that sort of thing.

So they were married, with the understanding that

Peter could still go on worshiping the very sound
of Eleanor Arling's name and turning white when
he came across a mention of her or of her pictures in
the cabled news of the art world in Paris. Flossie
was, so we all agreed, a good sport if there ever
was one, and she stuck gamely to her bargain. She
had transferred the big silver-framed photograph of
Miss Arling from Peter's bachelor quarters to the
wall of their new living room, and she dusted it as
conscientiously as she did the Botticelli Spring
which I gave her for a wedding present. It was not
easy for her. I have seen her flush deeply and set
her lips hard as Peter looked up at the dusky brooding eyes shadowed by the casque of black braids.
Flossie is one of the small, quick, humming-bird
women, with nothing to set against Miss Arling's
massive classic beauty, and by her expression at
such moments, I know she felt her defenselessness
bitterly. But she never let Peter see how she felt.
She had taken him, the darkness of his unrequited
passion heavy on him, and if she ever regretted it,
she gave no sign.

She flashed about the house, keeping it in perfect
order, feeding Peter the most delicious food, and
after the twins came, caring for them with no strain
or nervous tension, with only a bright thankful en-

joyment of them that was warm on your heart like sunshine. Peter enjoyed his pretty home and devoted wife and lively babies and excellent food. He began to lay on flesh, and to lose the haggard, gray leanness which, just after Miss Arling had gone away, had made people turn and look after him in the street. Architecture is, even when you are busy and successful as Peter is, a rather sedentary occupation, offering no resistance to such cooking as Flossie's. Peter's skin began to grow rosy and sleek, his hair from being rough and bristling, began to look smooth and glossy. It was quite beautiful hair as long as it lasted; but as the years went on and the twins began to be big children, it, unlike the rest of Peter, began to look thinner. Peter with a bald spot was queer enough, but before he was thirty-five it was not a mere spot, but all the top of his head. We thought it very becoming to him as it gave him a beneficent, thoughtful, kindly look, like a philosopher. And his added weight was also distinctly an improvement to his looks. We often said to each other that nobody would ever have thought that crazy-looking boy would make such a nice-looking man.

Flossie had not changed an atom. Those tiny, slight women occasionally remain stationary in looks as though they were in cold storage. She continued to worship Peter, and as he had made a good husband, we had nothing to say, although of course you never can understand what an excessively devoted wife sees in her husband, year after year. Flossie never mitigated in the least the extremity of her attention to Peter's needs. When he was called away on a business trip she always saw that his satchel was packed with just what he would need; and she would have risen from her grave to put exactly the right amount of cream and sugar into his coffee.

The rest of us had forgotten all about Miss Arling's connection with Peter, and had grown so used to the big photograph of the big, handsome woman that we did not see it any more, when one morning I found Flossie waiting for me as I came downstairs. She was very pale, with dark circles under her eyes. She was holding a newspaper in her clenched hand—the New York newspaper they had always taken on account of its full, gossipy "Happenings in the World of Art" column. Flossie opened it to that column now, and read in a dry voice :"American art lovers are promised a treat in the visit of the famous Eleanor Arling who arrives on the *Mauretania*. Miss Arling plans an extensive trip in her native country from which she has been absent for many years. She will visit New York, Pittsburgh, Chicago, Denver and San Francisco. Her keen artistic memory is shown by her intention of breaking her trip for a few days at . . ." Flossie's voice broke. . . . "She's coming *here!*" she gasped. Then collecting herself, she continued reading, "Miss Arling told our interviewer that she once passed some weeks there and remembers with pleasure a composition of cliff, water, and pine trees. She wishes to see it again."

"Cliff, water, and pine trees," repeated Flossie, her eyes blazing. "Of course *we* know it is nothing in the way of a *landscape* she is coming to see here!" I saw that her little fists were clenched. "I won't stand it!" she cried, "I won't stand it!"

But she looked horribly frightened all the same.

"What can you do?" I asked, sympathizing painfully with the poor little thing.

"I shall go to her the minute she reaches town."

This threw me into a panic, "What good would *that* do?" I cried, alarmed at the prospect of scenes and goings-on.

"I don't know! I don't know! If I see her, I can think of some way to make her go away and not . . ." she said wildly.

I hoped devoutly that she would settle down from this hysterical state of unreason, but three days after this she darted in, her face pinched, and told me that the time was now, and that she wanted me to be with her. . . . "I must have *some*body there," she said piteously.

I was thoroughly alarmed, protested, tried desperately to back out, but found myself in Flossie's car driving at a dangerous rate of speed towards Miss Arling's hotel.

We were shown into the sitting room of her suite, and sat down, both breathing hard. I am fond of Flossie and I was very sorry for her, but I certainly wished her at the other end of the world just then. If I had not feared she would have rushed to lock me in, I would have tried to escape even then, but before I could collect myself, the door opened, and a stout, middle-aged woman came in. Her straight gray hair was bobbed and hanging in strings around a very red, glistening face. It was terribly hot weather and she had, I suppose, just came in from the long motor trip. She had a lighted cigarette in one hand. Her cushiony shapeless feet were thrust into a pair of Japanese sandals. She distinctly waddled as she walked. We supposed that she was Miss Arling's companion, and I said, because Flossie was too agitated to speak, "We wished to speak to Miss Arling, please."

"I am Miss Arling," she said casually. "Won't you sit down?" I don't know what I did, but I heard Flossie give a little squeak like a terrified rabbit. So I hurried on, saying desperately the first thing that came into my mind. "We heard you were coming . . . in the newspapers . . . we are old residents here . . . a cliff, water, and pine trees. . . . I know the view . . . we thought perhaps we might show you where. . . ."

She was surprised a little at my incoherence and Flossie's strange face, but she was evidently a much-experienced woman-of-the-world, whom nothing could surprise very much. "Oh, that's very kind," she said civilly, tossing her cigarette butt away and folding her strong hands on her ample knees, "But I went that way on the road coming into town. I remembered it perfectly I find. I used it as the background in a portrait, some years ago."

She saw no reason for expanding the topic and now stopped speaking. I could think of nothing more to say. There was a profound silence. Our hostess evidently took us for tongue-tied, small-town people who do not know how to get themselves out of a room, and went on making conversation for us with a vague, fluent, absent-minded kindness. "It's very pleasant to be here again. I stayed here once, you know, a few weeks, many years ago, when I was young. We had quite a jolly time, I remember. There was a boy here . . . a slim, dark, tall fellow, with the most perfect early-Renaissance head imaginable, quite like the Jeune Homme Inconnu. I've been trying all day to remember his name? Paul? . . . no. Walter? . . . it had two syllables it seems to me. Well, at any rate, he had two great beauties, the pale, flat white of his skin, and his great shaggy mass of dark hair. I've often used his hair in drawings, since. But I don't suppose he looks like that now."

Flossie spoke. She spoke with the effect of a revolver discharging a bullet, "Oh, yes, he does! He looks exactly like that still, only more mature, more interesting," she said in an indignant tone.

"Ah, indeed," said the painter with an accent of polite acquiescence. She sighed now and looked firmly at the clock. I rose and said since we could not be of use to her, we would leave her to rest.

She accompanied us to the door pleasantly enough, with the professional, impersonal courtesy of a celebrity.

Outside Flossie sprang into her car, leaving me

stranded on the sidewalk. "I must get Peter away," she said between her teeth.

"But not now, surely!" I cried.

"Now more than ever," she flung back at me, as she whirled the car around.

Then as I stood open-mouthed, utterly at a loss, she drove the car close to the curb and leaning to my ear, whispered fiercely, "You don't suppose I'd let him see how she looks *now*."

Miss Arling was gone before they returned from the two-day fishing-trip on which they started that night. I doubt if Peter ever heard that she had been in town.

The morning after their return, as soon as Peter had gone downtown, Flossie tore down the big photograph from the wall and flung it into the garbage can.

I noticed its absence some days later, when I went over to see them, and asked with a little apprehension, "What did Peter say when he found it gone?"

The strangest expression came into her face. She said in a low tone, "He has never even missed it." And then she began to cry. As I looked at her, I saw that she had suddenly begun to show her age.

SUPPLY AND DEMAND

THE thoughtful intellectual people around the fire were talking with animation and conviction, and I hoped the one business-man present, a relative of mine, was appreciating his privileges. It was not often that you could collect before your fire so many brilliant people representing so many important varieties of human activity; and when you had collected them it was not often that the talk fell on a subject big enough to draw out of each one his most hotly held conviction.

The subject was big enough in all conscience: nothing more or less than what is the matter with the world in general and with our country in particular. They all had different ideas about what the trouble is and about the best cure for it. The head nurse of the big City Hospital had started the ball rolling by some of her usual scornful remarks about the idiocy with which most people run their physical lives, and the super-idiocy, as she put it, "which makes them think that doctors and nurses can put scrambled eggs back into the shell."

"We'll never have any health as a nation till we

have health as individuals," she said. "See that the babies have clean milk; give the children plenty of space and time for out-door play; keep the young folks busy with athletic sports; run down all the diphtheria carriers and make it a misdemeanor not to be both vaccinated for small-pox and inoculated against typhoid . . . and we'd be a nation such as the world never saw before."

The political reformer was sincerely shocked by the narrowness of her views, and took her down in a long description of our villainously mismanaged government. "Much good mere physical health would do against our insane tolerance of such political ineptness and corruption!" he ended. "What we need is an awakening to the importance of government as every man's personal business."

Mrs. Maynard, the tragic-faced, eloquent Scotch expert on birth-control, now said in that low, bitter voice of hers which always makes every one stop to listen, "I would be obliged if you would point out to me how either physical health or the very best of municipal governments should alleviate in the slightest, the hideous ulcers of our so-called respectable married homes. When the very foundation of every-day human life is cemented in such unthinkable cruelty and suffering to defenseless women, I

don't see how human beings with hearts in their
bosoms can stop for an instant to consider such
puerile non-essentials as athletics and party politics!"

The two or three happily married women in the
group, startled by her fierce acrimony, were silent,
feeling abashed by the grossly comfortable way we
had managed to escape even a knowledge of the horrors which she so urgently assured us were universal.
But Mr. Sharpless, the efficiency engineer, shook his
head pityingly. "No, no, my dear lady, you can't
cure anything by going at it with the hammer and
tongs of direct action. The economic key is the only
one that fits all locks, opens all doors. The women
of what we call the 'upper classes' do not suffer as
you describe. You know they don't. Now why do
we *call* them the 'upper classes'? Because they
have money. You know it! Hence, if everybody
had money . . . ! I tell you the thing to do is to
reorganize our wretched old producing machinery
till ever so much more is produced, ever so much
more easily; and then invent distributing machinery
that will ensure everybody's getting his share. You
may not think home life is much affected by the
chemist in his laboratory, devising a way to get nitro-
gen chiefly from the air, or by the engineer strug-

gling with the problem of free power out of the tides
or the sun. But it is. Just once put *all* women in
the comfortable upper classes. . . ."

He was interrupted here by a number of protest-
ing voices, all speaking at once, the loudest of which,
Professor Oleny's finally drowned out the others,
". . . money without intelligence is the most fatal
combination conceivable to man! Economic prosperity would spell speedy destruction without an
overhauling of education." He spun like a pin-
wheel for a moment, in a sparkling, devastating
characterization of American schools, and of their
deadening effect on the brains which passed through
them, and began on a description of what schools
should be.

But I had heard him lecture on that only the day
before and, looking away from him, sought out the
face of my cousin, the business-man. He had sat
through it all, and now continued to sit through the
free-for-all debate which followed, without opening
his mouth except to emit an occasional thoughtful
puff of cigar-smoke. His thoughts seemed to be
with the billowing smoke-rings, which he sent towards the ceiling rather than with the great sweep
of the subjects being discussed. I knew well enough
that his silence did not come in the least from any

inability to follow the pyrotechnics about him, and I felt in his absent preoccupation something of the disdain, traditionally felt for talkers and reformers by men of action—when in the twentieth century and in the United States, you say "man of action" you mean of course, "businessman."

It nettled me a little, and after the others had gone and he was finishing the end of his cigar, I said challengingly, "I suppose you think they are all off! I suppose you think that you know what is the matter with the world and that it is something quite different."

He considered the end of his cigar meditatively and answered mildly, "I don't *think* I know, I *know* I know."

"Oh, you do, do you?" I said, amused and ironic. "Would you mind telling me what it is?"

He shucked further down in his chair, tipped his head back and looked up at the ceiling. "Well, if you really want to know, I'll tell you a story that happened just lately in one of the biggest mailorder houses in this country. Of course, I know that you don't fully appreciate the importance of mail-order houses, not being in business. And they're too through and through American a growth

for people like your friends to-night to know about
or talk about. But some of the best brains and real
sure-enough genius in the United States have gone
into creating the mail-order house idea. Maybe you
might allow that to be a good enough reason for
considering for a moment what goes on inside one
of them . . . what?

"As a matter of fact, the story isn't just about a
mail-order house, but about what is the matter with
the world . . . the very same subject your friends
were debating. My story won't have so many long
words in it as they use, nor so many abstract ideas
. . . at least on the surface; but it won't do you
any harm to soak it away and think it over. I'll tell
you what, *I've* been thinking it over this evening, as
I listened to the talk. I only heard the story this
morning, and it's stuck in my head all day . . .
and especially this evening, as they were all talking
about how to hit on some organization of society
that would really fix things up, once and for all."

He paused for a moment, stretched his legs out
straight before him and put his hands into his
pockets. "If I really told you all you ought to
know, to understand the background and setting of
the story, I'd be sitting here to-morrow morning still
talking. So I won't try, I'll just tell you the plain

story as it happened. You try to imagine the background: an organization as big, as complicated, with as many chances for waste motion, or overorganization, or poor organization as society itself. And not only power and glory, but *cash*, plenty of hard cash as immediate reward for the successful use of brains.

"Well now, into that arrives a smart youngster full of enthusiasm for making things run better, just like your friends to-night; dead sure just like them that *he* has the key; with lots of pep and brains and interest in his job, pushing his way right up from the stenographer's desk, with his eye on the Manager's. Do you get him? Well, he's laid awake nights, thinking how to improve the organization, partly because he wanted to improve it, partly because he wanted to get the credit for it . . . just like your friends again. And because he is a smart young fellow as keen as a razor, he soon figured out a way to increase business, to increase it like a house afire, and to handle it once it was increased.

"He went to the big man of the concern and laid out his plans. Now, you'd better believe the big men in any organization always have a glad hand out for anybody in the concern who'll show interest and brains; and the boy got treated like a king. Sure, he could try out his plan! On a small scale at first, to see how it would work. Let him take a county out of each of six selected states, and concentrate on them. And, sure, yes, indeed, he could have anything in the organization he wanted, to make his try with.

"So the boy went away bounding like a rubber-ball and planned his campaign. I won't bother you by trying to tell you what it was. . . . It wouldn't interest you, and anyhow you couldn't understand the business details. It was a mixture of intensive publicity, special attention paid to detail, a follow-up system that meant personal care and personal acquaintance with the tastes of customers, and intimate knowledge of what past orders from customers had been. To get the right kind of assistants he went through the various departments of that big organization and hand-picked his staff; the very best of the publicity men, the smartest of the order-clerks, the brightest of the stenographers. And then they just tore in and ate up the territory they were practising on! They plowed it with publicity, and sowed it with personal service, they reaped, by George, a harvest that would put your eye out! Business increased by a twenty-five per cent, by a fifty per cent! At the end of a year, the boy, too big for his skin, paraded into the Manager-in-chief's office with statistics to prove a seventy-five per cent increase over any business ever done there before! Well, that was simply grand, wasn't it? Yes, the Manager would certainly sit up and take some notice of a system that had accomplished *that!*"

My cousin had finished his cigar, now threw the butt into the fire-place, and sat looking at the embers with a somber expression. I couldn't see anything to look somber about. Indeed I found myself stifling a yawn. What did I care how much business a mail-order house did or how they did it?

My cousin answered my thought, "Don't you see that the story is all about the same general idea you were all discussing this evening? It is about getting things done more intelligently, more efficiently, about avoiding fool mistakes, about rising to big opportunities, about learning how to scramble over the obstacles that prevent human beings from being intelligent and efficient and effective. Now, then, at the first take-off, the boy had soared right over those obstacles, hadn't he? But the Manager-in-chief knew a thing or two about them, too. In fact he had grown bald and gray trying to climb over those very same obstacles. But you can be sure the boy didn't once think that his chief might be just as anxious as he was to have things done better.

Boys never do. . . ." There was a pause, while my cousin considered the embers moodily.

"So, by and by, after the boy had fizzed the place all foamy with his wonderful statistics, the bald-headed, gray-haired Manager began to come down to brass tacks, and to inquire just how the thing had been done. The boy was crazy to tell him, went into every detail; and the Manager listened hard.

"And then he shook his old bald gray head. He said: 'Young fellow, you listen to me. It takes *sense* to run that system of yours. You're counting on everybody, from you right down to the boy that works your mimeograph, paying attention to what he's doing, using his brains and using them every minute. If everybody doesn't, you won't get your results, will you? Now, consider this, how did you get hold of a staff that would have any brains to use and would use them? *You* know how! We let you run a fine tooth comb through our whole organization, thousands and thousands of employees. You took out of every department the very best they had; three or four out of hundreds, and they are the only ones out of thousands who amount to anything after years of training at our expense. And then you put your very best licks into it yourself. Now, who are you? You're the first stenog-

rapher we've had in ten years, who took enough
interest in the business as a whole to have a single
idea about it. You tell me something. Suppose we
reorganized along your lines, who would I get to
run all the other departments and keep up the high-
speed efficiency and red-hot ambition you've shown,
which is the *only* reason your scheme works? You
know as well as I do I can't find another *one*, let
alone the eighty or ninety I'd have to have, if we
tried to do business on your plan. And if I could—
supposing for the sake of argument that an angel
from Heaven served such department heads to me
on a silver platter, where am I going to find staffs to
work with them. You've *got* all the really efficient
employees we've been able to rake in from the whole
United States in the past twenty years.

" 'Did you ever have to work with a plain, ordinary six-for-a-quarter stenographer, such as the business colleges turn out, such as you mostly get?
You've built your machine so that only brains and
sense will run it. How long would it take a couple
of hundred of such stenogs to smash your system
into splinters? Did you ever have to try and get
work out of the average dressy young employee who
puts ninety-eight and a half per cent of what gray
matter he has on his neckties and the bets he made

on the horse-races, and the little flier he took on stocks; and one and a half per cent of his brains on his work when somebody higher up is looking at him? How do you suppose you can persuade a crowd of light-weights like that to care a whoop whether Mrs. Arrowsmith in Cohoes, N. Y., is satisfied with the color of the linoleum rug she bought?' "

My cousin looked at me hard, and again answered an unspoken thought of mine. "Are you wondering why hadn't the boy interrupted long before this, to hold up his end, if he was really so enthusiastic as I've said? This is the reason. Though he hadn't let on to the Manager, he really had had plenty of troubles of his own, already, keeping even his hand-picked crew up to the scratch. Many's the time he'd been ready to murder them! Drive as hard as he might, he couldn't keep them steadily up to the standard he'd set for his work. He'd noticed that. Oh, yes, of course, he'd noticed it all right, and he'd been furious about it. But until that minute, he hadn't thought of it—what it meant; and the minute the Manager spoke, he knew in his bones the old man was right. And he felt things come down with a smash.

"It pretty nearly knocked him silly. He never

said a word. And the old bald-head looked at him,
and saw that in the last three minutes the boy had
grown up . . . he'd grown up! That hurts, hurts
more than any visit to the dentist. I know how
he felt; probably the Manager knew how he felt.
Anybody who's ever tried to get anything done has
run his head into that stone wall.

"Well, he was sorry for the kid, and tried to let
him down easy. He went on talking, to give the
boy time to catch his breath. 'You understand, I'd
like, maybe more than you, to reorganize the whole
ball o' wax, on any lines that would work better.
And there are lots of good points in your plan that
we *can* use, plenty of 'em. This invention of yours
about cross-indexing orders now, that is a splendid
idea. I believe we could install that . . . it looks
almost fool proof! And maybe we might run a special mailing-list along the lines you've worked out.
Lemme look at it again. Well, I guess the mistakes
the stenogs would make *might* be more than offset
by the extra publicity . . . maybe!'

"But the lad was feeling too cut up to pay any
attention to these little poultices. He stood there,
and almost fell in pieces, he was thinking so hard.
Not very cheerful thoughts, at that. When he
could get his breath he leaned over the table and

said in a solemn, horrified voice, 'Good God, Mr. Burton, why then . . . why then . . .' He was all but plumb annihilated by the hardness of the fact that had just hit him on the head. He broke out, 'What's the *use* of inventing a better system as long as . . . as long as . . . ?' he got it out finally. 'Why, Mr. Burton, there just aren't enough folks with sense to go around!' "

My cousin stood up, moved to the hall, secured his hat and looked in at me through the door-way. "Poor kid!" he commented pityingly. "Just think of his never having thought of that before!"

UNCLE ELLIS

I NEVER saw my Uncle Ellis because he died before
I was born, but I heard a great deal about him when
I was a child. His stepdaughter married one of our
fellow-townsmen, and lived next door to us when I
was a little girl, and her mother, my great-aunt,
Uncle Ellis' third wife, lived with her. Whatever
Cousin Ruth did not say about her stepfather, Aunt
Molly supplied. The two women spent the rest of
their lives hating him, and for his sake hated, dis-
trusted and despised all men.

The gruesome impressions of married life which
float through the air to most little girls, came to me
from their half-heard and half-understood stories of
Uncle Ellis. He had killed his first two wives, they
said, just as much as though he had taken an ax
to them, and only his opportune death had saved
Aunt Molly from the same fate. His innumerable
children—I would never venture to set down how
many he had, all in legal marriage—feared and de-
tested him and ran away from home as soon as they
could walk. He was meanness itself, secret, sneak-

ing meanness, the sort of man who would refuse his wife money for a wringer to do the family wash, and spend five dollars on a box of cigars; he would fly into a black rage over a misplaced towel, and persecute the child who had misplaced it, till she was ready to commit suicide; and then open his arms with a spectacular smile to the new baby of a parishioner. After mistreating his wife till she could hardly stand, she used to hear him holding forth in a boys' meeting, exhorting them to a chivalry attitude towards women.

Aunt Molly died long ago, firing up to the last in vindictive reminiscences of her husband. Ruth is dead now, too, in the fullness of time. I am a middle-aged woman, and probably the only one now alive who ever heard those two talk about Uncle Ellis; and I had forgotten him. If he stayed at all in my memory it was with the vague, disembodied presence of a character in a book.

About a month ago, I accepted an invitation to speak at a convention in a town in the middle-west which I had never seen, but the name of which seemed slightly familiar; perhaps, I thought, because I had learned it in a geography lesson long ago. But when I arrived I understood the reason. It was the town where for many years Uncle Ellis had been pastor of the church. At the railway station, as I stepped down on the platform, one of the older women in the group who met me, startled me by saying, "We have been especially anxious to see you because of your connection with our wonderful Dr. Ellis Randolph. I was a young girl when he died, but I can truly say that my whole life has been influenced for good by the words and example of that saintly man."

The elderly man beside her added, "You will find many here who will say the same. In the formative period of our town's history he made an indelible impression for good."

They took me to his church, where a large bronze tablet set forth his virtues and his influence. They showed me the Ellis Randolph Memorial Library. I was shown the public playground which he conceived a generation before any one else thought of such a thing. But what made the deepest impression on me were the men and women who came to shake my hand because I was Uncle Ellis' niece, because they wanted to testify to the greatness of his value in their lives. The minister of the town, a white-haired man, told me with a deep note of emotion in his voice, that Dr. Randolph had done more than merely save his life; in his wayward youth he had saved his soul alive. The banker told me that he had heard many celebrated orators, but never any one who could go straight to the heart like Dr. Randolph. "I often tell my wife that she ought to be thankful to Dr. Randolph for a lecture on chivalry to women which he gave to us boys, at an impressionable moment of our lives."

And the old principal of the school said, "Not a year goes by that I do not thank God for sending that righteous man to be an example to my youth. He left behind him many human monuments to his glory."

What did I say to them? Oh, I didn't say anything to them. I couldn't think of anything to say.

GOD'S COUNTRY

WHEN I was a faculty-child living in a middle-western university town we were all thrilled by the news that the energetic Chancellor of the University had secured as head of the Department of Chemistry a noted European scientist. Although still young he had made a name for himself by some important discoveries in organic chemistry. We talked about those discoveries as fluently, and understood about them as thoroughly as we all now discuss and understand the theories of Professor Einstein.

Professor Behrens was not only a remarkable chemist, so we heard, but a remarkable teacher and a man of wide sympathies and democratic ideals. It was the candid period in American life, when, especially in the west, the word "Europe" was pronounced with a very special intonation, of which Henry James' wistful admiration was the quintessence. It was the time in American university life when Germany was the goal toward which all our younger scholars ran their fastest race. Yet here was Professor Behrens, leaving a University not only European but German, from which our younger

professors were proud to have a Ph.D. and deliber-
ately choosing our new, raw, young institution for
the sake of the free, untrammeled, democratic life
in America. It went to our heads!

Passages in his letter of acceptance were read to
my mother by my father, who had borrowed the letter from the Chancellor. "I have a family of children and as they grow older I am more and more
aware of the stifling, airless stagnation of European
life. I want them to know something bigger and
freer than will ever come to them in this Old World
of rigid caste lines and fixed ideas. My wife and I,
too, wish to escape from the narrowness of this pro-
vincial town where an arrogant young lieutenant
swaggering about in his gold-braided white broadcloth uniform is much higher in social rank than
the most learned and renowned member of the University faculty; where a rich lumber-merchant,
brutal and ignorant, can buy his way into political
position and parade about with sash and gold chain
and the insignia of the office of Mayor."

We were all righteously indignant over such elements of life in Europe, and quite exalted in our
certainty that the distinguished immigrant would
find nothing like that in our midst. The sole and
only representative of the military caste was the

lieutenant who drilled the university battalion, and he was a most unassuming young American who never on any occasion wore white broadcloth, put on his plain dark-blue uniform as seldom as possible, and for the most part wore a pepper-and-salt business suit and a derby hat. Since there were no trees on the Western plains, there was no equivalent to the iniquitous lumber merchant, the nearest approach being a man who had made a good deal of money out of lucky guesses in real estate. But he would have dropped dead before putting on a sash and a gold chain.

So we awaited the Behrens full of pride and pleasure. When they arrived, everybody in the faculty gave receptions and lunch-parties for them, and all we children rejoiced in the unlimited leavings of fried chicken (it was in September), ice cream, and cake, which were at our disposition after these "functions," as the Faculty ladies called them. Although surprisingly unceremonious as to table manners, the Behrens were as nice as we expected to find them; and they were evidently delighted with the warm-hearted, open-handed good nature of Americans, by the cordiality of their reception (which seemed quite to amaze them) by the wide-open doors which led anywhere they might wish to go, by the absence of class distinction, and by the generosity with which America supported universities, hospitals, libraries, and public schools. When the University opened, Professor Behrens threw himself into his teaching and soon became one of the favorite professors. He had a song sung about him at the winter concert of the Glee Club; and the Junior year-book was dedicated to him in the spring. By that time the Behrens children, who were in the eighth, fifth, and third grades of my public school were no longer to be distinguished from the rest of us, running and yelling on the hard-beaten earth of the playground, and thoroughly acquainted with duck-on-a-rock, prisoner's base, and run-sheep-run. Julie and I were classmates in the fifth grade that year, and the next and the next.

But just as we were about to pass together into the exalted rank of the eighth grade, Professor Behrens received a call to be Rector (Julie explained to me that this had nothing to do with a church, but was the same as our Chancellor) of a university in his own country.

It seemed such an advancement to be promoted from Professor to Chancellor that it was no surprise to have him accept, and to see Mrs. Behrens begin hastily to pack up the family belongings. But

what did surprise us was the sudden revelation
brought out by this event, of a great home-sickness
on the part of the Behrens to get back to a "civilized
country." This was one of the phrases Julie overheard her father saying to her mother, which she repeated to me, and I to my parents. A faculty circle
gets its news by about the same channels as an army
post or a village sewing circle. So by the time this
remark had reached my parents it did not surprise
them. The Behrens, although still heartily grateful for all the kindness that had been shown them,
although still feeling a lively affection for the good-
hearted qualities in American life, could not conceal
their immense relief at the prospect of the change.
Professor Behrens discussed the question with the
open frankness of a scientist before a new phenomenon: "I had no idea, till I had to go without them,
how vital to civilization are the finer shades, the
polish, the stability, the decorum, which comes only
with long life of a society in an old country. I had
never thought of them, had always supposed, of
course, they were to be found everywhere. It is not
that I blame America for not having them . . .
nothing but time can give them . . . but there is
no denying that they give a different color to life,
the same difference of color there is between camping

out in a cave, ever so fine and airy and open a cave, and living in a well-ordered house with the appurtenances of civilization. There is a certain something which springs up from such niceties of life . . . I can hardly wait to get home, and give a real dinner with well-trained servants, and cultivated, established guests who have had a social position for so long that it is a part of them. The crudeness, the abruptness, the roughness in human intercourse here! And the total lack on the part of people in the lower classes of any sense of the fitness of things! The *conductor on the street-car* slapped me on the back the other day!"

So we gave them a grand good-by reception in the gymnasium, and we faculty-children fairly swam in lemonade and wallowed in left-over cake. The faculty presented Professor Behrens with a beautifully bound edition of Emerson, and Mrs. Behrens with a little pearl pendant; and then they went away, and we supposed we would never see them again.

Julie and I corresponded once in a while as children do, the letters growing less frequent as Julie evidently began to forget her English. Mrs. Behrens wrote back a round-robin letter or two to be passed about among her faculty friends, one of them describing the splendid, ceremonious, Old-World way in which Professor Behrens was inducted into his new position. She spoke with special pride of the way in which both the military and municipal authorities of the town had turned out to do him honor, the soldiers, officers, and the Mayor of the town marching at the head of the procession, the latter in his bright sash and gold chain of office. It seemed to us we had heard something about that Mayor before, but we could not remember what it was.

And then Julie forgot her English altogether, and Mrs. Behrens' letters dwindled and there were none.

I got on through the eighth grade and went into the University prep-school. After three years there, my father was called to a better position in another State University. As we were settling ourselves in the new home, what should we hear but that a distinguished European scientist was about to be added to the faculty, none other than Professor Behrens.

Foreigners, even distinguished ones, were more common in American faculties then than they had been seven years before; there was a large German Department, with many native German instructors; and the University was further east and hence not so open-heartedly welcoming. There was, therefore,

no such stir over the newcomers as on their first arrival although every one was very nice to them and
the President's wife had Mrs. Behrens stand by her
in the receiving line at the first of the faculty receptions. But the Behrens did not seem to notice
that there was anything lacking in their treatment.
You never saw people more delighted than they were
to be back in America.

"It was worse than I remembered," Professor
Behrens told my father. "After an experience of
the free, breezy, self-respecting life in America it
was simply unendurable. Suffocating, simply suffocating! With the most ridiculous caste spirit.
Rusted to a stand-still with cock-sure conservatism!
An instant, hermetic closing up of every pore at any
mention of new possibilities for human nature, or
for human organizations. And such absurd, stiff,
artificial rules of conduct and precedence in society!
Let me tell you an episode which will seem almost
incredible to you, but which really decided us to
come back here. At a garden party my wife . . .
my wife! . . . seeing there the wife of the General
commanding the troops in the town garrison and
knowing her quite well, stepped across the lawn to
speak to her, one lady to another. Will you believe
it, because she had not waited till the General's wife

had summoned her to her circle, my poor wife received a cold, unrecognizing stare, her outstretched hand was left hanging in the air, and the General's wife turned her back on her. And when I was furious and protested, I was made uncomfortable, seriously uncomfortable!"

And Mrs. Behrens told my mother she had been horrified by the cold-hearted envy, hatred and meanness which lay underneath the polished manners of many of the people in their circle. "They do not wish you well. They wish you ill. They simply have no conception of the meaning of that American word 'friendly.'"

Julie was ready for the University, as I was, and we entered the Freshman class together. She was a very pretty girl, one of the brown-haired Teutons, who are so much finer and more neatly finished than the blonde ones, and she had her fair share of popularity. We were taken into the same fraternity, studied together, and were much in each other's homes. I soon saw that the Behrens home was not altogether a light-hearted one. After the first flush of pleasure at being back had passed, a cloud of depression settled over them. Their sojourn in a more finished and stable, low-toned and nuanced civilization had put them all out of key for the loud-

mouthed, cheerful American tune. They found it
shrill and noisy, and often stopped their ears against
it. Heavens, they had not remembered that American trades-people were so utterly mannerless! Nor
that all Americans were so blackly ignorant of the
arts! They had no interest in organized athletics,
and very soon developed an active hostility for foot-
ball because of the indisputable fact that the university world was so occupied with it, that nothing
serious was done in classes until after Thanksgiving
when the last game was played. The Behrens were
musical and nobody in the city cared for music except the German-Americans in their shabby quarter at the other end of town, and they were fat gro-
cers, saloon-keepers or foremen in factories, people
with whom the Behrens could not dream of asso-
ciating. They were really very miserable and lonely
and disillusioned.

When we were Seniors there came a wonderful
offer from Germany: a very high Government position for Professor Behrens. I heard them discussing this with a certain indecision which I had never
heard in their remarks before. They knew very
well what was before them in Germany. But, oh,
what was about them here! The very servant problem alone made it impossible for civilized beings to

organize a livable existence in America. Not to
speak of a thousand other, raw, unfinished edges
which rasped and fretted them at every turn.

They finally decided to go, but their packing-up
was conducted in a very different spirit from the first
one I had seen. They had begun to divine that there
was, in this business of looking for the ideal country, something more than meets the eye.

I happened to visit them a few years after this,
just before I was married, and found them much
dissatisfied with European life. Mrs. Behrens was
nettled and fretted by the question of social precedence which was, so it seemed to her, constantly
used to humiliate her; and the children were stifling
in the restricted, fenced-in, tyrannically regulated
corner of life which was theirs. Julie took me off
for a long walk one afternoon and told me something
of her opinion of European young men, especially
the officers whom for the most part she met in society, as they were the ones who had most leisure for
afternoon and evening parties. "I can just tell you
one thing," she said with a grim accent and a hard-
set jaw, "I'll never marry a European, if I die an
old maid!"

But later on, when her mother and she were exchanging reminiscences about the difficulties of American housekeeping, Julie cried out, "Oh, I couldn't keep house in a country where there is no servant class!"

Mrs. Behrens sighed, "Yes, I know, but just remember the bath-rooms, and the vacuum cleaners, and the hot water."

It seemed to me, as I looked about on their much-traveled chairs and tables that I saw them patiently making ready for another journey.

INHERITANCE

ONE of my mother's distant cousins was left a widow, years ago with no assets but the house she lived in, a savings-bank account, and a very pretty daughter, then eighteen years old. Cousin Henrietta's decisions were always prompt. It took her about six weeks to sell the house, draw the money from the savings-bank and take her daughter to Europe. I think her intention probably was to give Ella the benefit of a year's polish, and bring her back to the home market, her value enhanced by the reputation of her Continental "Education." But the impossible happened, as energetic women like Cousin Henrietta can occasionally make it happen. Through some chance connection at the pension in Florence, they made the acquaintance of a wealthy, middle-aged Tuscan, not the traditional European nobleman at all, but a swarthy, well-preserved man of the people, risen to wealth by his own exertions. He was presented to Ella and lost his head entirely over her pale blonde prettiness. He was fifty-five. They were married on her nineteenth birthday.

Cousin Henrietta shared their married life with them, of course, although this did not last very long. Signor Cattaneo, as not infrequently happens to elderly husbands of very young wives, tried to renew his youth too rapidly. He danced all one evening with his bride, an exercise which his great bulk made extremely violent for him; stepped out upon a balcony with her, in a cool, damp wind, and died of double pneumonia at the end of a week.

Cousin Henrietta still in charge of affairs, at once brought home to the God's country of Chicago, the lovely, wealthy little widow. They set up housekeeping on a grand scale with the money which was sent to them every month from the honest, conscientious Tuscan agent in Florence. The agent got it from the honest, conscientious Tuscan peasants, and they got it out of their bodies, sweating and toiling endlessly long hours in all weathers. Ella and Cousin Henrietta had everything they could think of, that money could buy; and presently Ella, wanting something new, bought herself a husband. He did not turn out very well: Ella had done exactly as she pleased for too long to bother with a husband, and after a time they separated, though there was never any legal action taken, since Cousin Henrietta was an extremely orthodox church member, who disapproved of any laxity in the relations between the sexes. Divorce seemed to her such a laxity.

Then Ella wanted to do as other wealthy and fashionable ladies do and learn how to ride. They bought, as usual, the best that money could buy, and this time it was a little too good for Ella; for the high-spirited thorough-bred took fright one day and, disregarding Ella's amateur efforts to control him, ran away, threw Ella off and broke her poor little neck.

Cousin Henrietta was horrified and scandalized to find that now Ella's remote but still legal husband would inherit a very large proportion of the Italian property. Her whole soul and being rose up wildly in an understandable and instinctive protest against this iniquity. She simply could not believe that the law would countenance such a barefaced theft of other people's property. She filled the newspapers and the courts with her clamor and made us all ashamed of the family name. But that was all the good it did her. Ella had not dreamed of making a will; Cousin Henrietta's son-in-law had no reason to love his wife's mother, and could see no reason why she had any more right to that fortune than he had. Neither can I, when it comes to that.

Ella's husband was rather dazed by his good luck

and made all haste to marry. But he did not make quite haste enough. That was one of the years when the influenza was going the rounds, and he died of it two days before his wedding, in spite of all the care of three trained nurses and a whole battery of consulting physicians. I never knew what became of his fiancée, but always wondered if she did not perhaps go to live with Cousin Henrietta, as being the only person who would entirely sympathize with her.

So the Cattaneo fortune passed to the casual next-of-kin, who happened to be the only nephew of Ella's husband, a young clerk of twenty. The honest conscientious agent in Florence, who was paid a small annual salary for his services, and who would have died before touching a penny not his, went on administering the Italian estate which was growing steadily in value all the time, and paying more income. He sent that income over to the new name and address in America. He was upheld in his meager, narrow, difficult life by feeling that he was living up to the fine old Tuscan code of honor; and he often told his children, who lacked schooling and opportunities he could have given them if he had had more money, that the best inheritance a father can leave his children is an unblemished name.

The children of Ella's husband's nephew have something much more substantial as an inheritance than that. For the young man with a fortune was married by a competent, ambitious girl as soon as he came of age. They have three children, who learned very young how to spend a great deal of money with great speed. The money which the Italian day-laborers and small-farmers earn by patient endurance of hardships, by eating rough, poor, scanty food, by working their pregnant wives to the day before their confinements, by taking their children out of school before they can read, is sent month by month to America and spent in buying a new fur set for Ella's husband's nephew's young-lady daughter, a ten-thousand-dollar racing-car for Ella's husband's nephew's seventeen-year-old son, and to keep Ella's husband's nephew from doing anything more strenuous than clipping the end of his cigars.

THIRTY YEARS AFTER

A LONG time ago, when Duane Bellamy was at the height of his brilliant fame, and when I was a little girl, his daughter chanced to be a school-mate of mine for a winter. And one Sunday evening I was invited to their supper-table. I was very much impressed by the momentous occasion which it seemed to me, and I have not forgotten a word he said, nor a gesture he made, nor an expression of his face. I can still see his darkly handsome face, with his glossy black mane, his large bright eyes, his great curling Assyrian beard. And if ever I saw a human being saturated to the bone with satisfaction, it was at that Sunday evening supper. He was acclaimed as the greatest portrait painter in America, and he accepted this well-deserved reputation with no mock modesty. The knowledge of it did not make him coarsely vain or puffed up. It acted on him like a generous wine, made him extravagantly kind and over-flowing with high spirits. His little girl told me that night that her princely father had been known to stop a tired coal-heaver at his work, hand him a twenty-dollar bill and walk on. He was like a great fountain of enjoyment, splashing with its clear waters all who came near it, even the little school-girl at the other end of the table.

But there were people he could not help to enjoyment. The name of one of them came up in the conversation that evening: "Poor old Hendricks!" said our host, "what can you do for the poor old chap? *He* doesn't even know what hit him!"

One of the younger painters there was a protégé of Bellamy's, admiring him so greatly that his paintings were scarcely to be told from his master's. He now answered, "Oh, the old Rip Van Winkle! He ought to be told to crawl into his hole and pull it in after him. Making a laughing-stock of himself with those sooty old landscapes of his, year after year."

Our host took a great draught of the beer in his stein, wiped his great mustache with his fine damask napkin, and turned comfortably in his chair, "Hendricks got me in a tight place the other day," he began, "At this year's exhibition he marched me up to one of his bitumen-black, woolly horrors, and said, 'Now, Bellamy, you're an honest man. Tell me what it is you youngsters don't like in that? It looks all right to me. I can't see why they all jump

on me so. I look at theirs, and then I look at mine.
. . . I *can't* see what they're talking about.' "

"Well, for God's sake, what nerve!" ejaculated
the disciple, very much astonished. "What did you
say?"

"What could I say?" said Bellamy. "I didn't
want to hurt the old man's feelings. I hadn't supposed till then that he'd so much as noticed how
people feel about his work. I didn't try to explain
to him, of course. What's the use? He *can't* understand! If I'd talked to him all day about what
we're after—light, and shimmer, and vibration—
he wouldn't have known what I was talking about.
If it were *in* him to understand, he'd die before he'd
paint the way he does. So I just patted him on the
back and said, 'Oh, you're all right, Mr. Hendricks.
What makes you think there is anything the matter
with your work?' and pretended that somebody was
calling to me from the other side of the gallery."

He finished his beer at a draught. He thought
himself magnificently kind and tolerant. And so
did we.

That was a long time ago, thirty years ago, to be
exact. The Bellamys took their little girl out of our
school that spring, and I saw no more of them. But

I always felt a slight personal interest at the sight
of his name in a list of exhibitors, and in picture-
galleries always went to look at whichever bright,
high-keyed, dashing portrait he was exhibiting that
year. Some years ago it began to seem to me that
they did not look just the same; and yet when I
looked straight at them, I saw that they were, quite
miraculously, the same, the old Bellamy flowing
brush-work, the masterly rendering of fabrics, the
ringing color, the firm drawing, all lighted by that
bold flood of sunlight with which he had shocked
and enchanted the early American public groping
its way out from Munich.

Presently, finding that the impression that they
were different persisted, I set myself to analyze it,
and found that their altered look came from the
altered character of the paintings beside and above
them . . . and then, as the years went on, below
them! For the time came when the annual Bellamy portrait was not in the center of the last gallery, to catch your eye as you entered, but was hung
high in one of the side-rooms. It looked very queer
and matter-of-fact with its solid surfaces honestly
rendered in all their opacity, compared to the odd,
subtle, sideways-glancing, arrestingly imaginative
canvases about it. They took the eye far below the

"THE OLD NEW ENGLAND STOCK"

STUDENTS and classifiers of American "types" often say that the grandfathers of the present generation of New Englanders represent the "New England type" much more accurately than their descendants of to-day. Some times I wonder what they mean by "New England type." Apparently they make the phrase stand for blue-nosed, thin-blooded frigidity of temperament, a pinched, mean, timorous attitude towards human life and human nature, and a cold, calculating capacity to skin other people alive in a bargain. At any rate, the presumption seems to be that whatever else they were, New Englanders were always very much of the same sort.

Here are my two New England grandfathers.

Both of them had identically the same sort of ancestry, plain English people who came to the New World about the middle of the seventeenth century. Certain genealogically-minded members of the two families have gathered reverently together the scant tradition concerning the generations that bridge the two centuries and a half of life in America; but though I have dutifully plodded through the thick volumes of "family histories" I have never been able to see that any of my forebears did anything more than earn their own livings and keep out of jail.

Younger branches of both families moved up into Vermont, after the end of the French-and-Indian wars and have lived here ever since. Both my grandfathers spent their boyhood on Vermont farms. And there the resemblance ceases.

One of them had, apparently, from early childhood, a passion for books and learning and sophistication and cultivation—and gregarious, articulate social existence—and dinner parties and black broadcloth and white linen and good wine—and all the other elements in the sort of life which is not to be found on Vermont farms. The Vermont farm, however, seems to have presented him with some tools for getting what he wanted: a powerful great body, an active mind and an unlimited amount of dynamic energy. He left home at sixteen (this was about 1833) spurred on by the sympathy of a strong-minded mother. I have still in the attic of his old house, the little hair-covered trunk which he took with him, and which contained all his worldly possessions.

From that time on, until his old age, he never came home except to rest in the occasional, very brief intervals of incessant and almost appalling activity, both intellectual and physical. With only a little help from his family he earned his way through college, and then put himself through a Theological Seminary in record time. With him, as with other manifestants of the mid-century explosion of energy in America, it was as if the long generations of vegetating country-dwellers had, like other vegetating matter of by-gone ages, turned to rich veins of highly combustible material, which this descendant of theirs mined out, at top speed, and cast by great shovelfuls into the furnace of his personality. He seems always to have been incandescent, the whole six-feet-three of him, with motive-power which he could not, try as he might, use up fast enough to cool off. All his life he burned hot with a vitality at which an ever-widening circle of other human beings, rich and poor, young and old, learned and ignorant, warmed their hands and their hearts. Even the people whom he furiously rubbed the wrong way (he had as many enemies as friends) were stimulated by the friction to a quicker life-pace, a livelier circulation. The temperature in a room rose when he entered it. Even people of sluggish, scholarly, dilettante temperaments, even coldly superior and skeptical people who prided themselves on being too disdainful of life to lift an eyebrow over its issues, soon kindled either to intense exasperation or lively personal affection. In either case, calm and ease and torpidity of life were scorched and shaken. I have often thought with sympathy of the vestrymen in Grandfather's various parishes.

As a young clergyman he ran one parish after another, with increasing brio. When he settled down in the New York parish where he stayed for most of his life, he was already editing a church-paper and writing innumerable pamphlets, in addition to his regular duties as rector. He now speeded up the staid old parish into new work of all sorts, added one mission chapel after another to the church organization, pushed out the influence of the parish further and further, especially into the outlying regions of the slums, which because of their very discouraging aspect of poverty and foreignness had been till then safe from attempts to improve them.

Of course I knew my grandfather only when he was a very old man, long after he had retired from active life; but I never got from him the slightest impression that he was what is known as a "religious-minded person" or that all this remarkable expansion of church and mission work came entirely from evangelical fervor. In fact, as I remember Grandfather, you never would dream that he had been a minister at all. My guess is that he developed that church as his contemporaries developed their transcontinental systems of railways, because he was born with a clutch that never slipped, so that all the power he created by his many-cylindered motor was transmitted without loss to the wheels which sent him with extreme rapidity along the road he had chanced to follow.

He not only developed the parish, he developed his own life: he bought books, unendingly bought books, Hebrew, Latin, Greek, French, English. No junk-man who ever lived has been able to free us entirely of this vast accumulation of serious-minded books of research, now quite worthless, all of them, full of the pompous and inaccurate scholarship of his day. He traveled abroad and sprang, tiger-like, upon European culture, with his formidable New-World capacity for the assimilation of Gargantuan meals of solid food. He married "well," as the saying goes, and gave his son university life and European travel. He lived as he had wanted to live, with friends and acquaintances in three countries, dressing his vast body in fine broadcloth and white linen; his house was lined with well-bound books; he was a famous talker—in the vein of Dr. Johnson—much sought after for his brilliantly amusing conversation, though at times, I take it, he followed his prototype into rather overpowering monologue; he was a powerful and very fluent public speaker —we have chests and chests full of his sermons still in the attic—and so far as I can gather he no more doubted the ultimately satisfying value of all these things as an integral part of life than Mr. Russel Sage seems to have questioned the ultimately satisfying value of squeezing the last penny of interest out of a loan, or Barnum to have doubted the worthwhileness of running the biggest show on earth.

It would be very unfair to give the impression that his agreeable social life and the possession of objects and books then in fashion made up the whole or even the largest part of his life. It took such a formidable number of elements to satisfy his huge appetite for life and activity, that it would be difficult to catalog them all. Controversy, for instance; he adored pamphleteering, and was known as one of the leading controversialists of his time.

He was a heart-felt Low-Churchman and perhaps the real passion of his passionate life was his hot-blooded detestation of formalism in religious beliefs. Infinitely various, and all headlong, were his attacks on High-Churchism, with its rigid orthodoxy, and its fol-de-rols (as he called them) of salvation by incense and candles and twiddling distinctions between green and blue and yellow stoles.

Indeed this shouldering impatience of formal theological points led him late in life, to disagree vigorously with the majority of his parishioners on several questions of doctrine. Refusing to conform to the strict pattern they wished to impose upon him, he blew up with an explosion, shook the dust of his religious vocation off his feet, and retired to the comfortable old house in Vermont, where he spent his old age, living comfortably on his small savings. He took with him all the possessions he had enjoyed so heartily, his many, many books, his substantial furniture, the excellent oil-portrait which had been painted of his vivid, handsome face in middle-life, his gold-headed cane, his great black-silk clerical robes, and fine ecclesiastical linen. When he died, he had never, so far as I know, slept out of an excellent bed a single night in all his life.

The other grandfather fared forth at about the same date or a little earlier, and at about the same age; but not in search of well-set dinner-tables nor well-filled libraries, nor the inheritance of culture from past ages. On the contrary, he seems all his life to have been engaged in running away from even the light and sketchy approximation to imprisoning regularity which was shown by the America of that day and the State of his birth. Like an unbroken colt who snorts and wheels and dashes away at the mere sight of some one emerging from the barn with a rope halter, this other farm-boy gave one look at what seemed to him the penitentiary-like pressure of conventional life and ran away with all the speed of what turned out to be a remarkably fleet pair of heels. First, as a lad, he ran away from his perfectly comfortable home, where he had been well cared for, and soundly if plainly educated. Disdaining . . . no, more than that, courting hardship, as he always did, he roamed out into the absolute, untrammeled freedom of early frontier life. There he starved and hunted and went in ragged buckskin, and trapped, and moved on, and grew up to a great height and great strength, and was no man's man to his heart's content. At some time during this period he acquired, with characteristic casual ease, the profession of surveyor, the only one of the trades or professions at which he was willing even to give a glance. There was plenty of unsurveyed land in the States at that time, and all of it in the new, untracked wilderness which he loved.

He seems always to have despised physical comfort as a clumsy trap laid by life to catch you and hold you fast. None of it for him. He hated the very indoor smell of it, as he did the burdening weight of material possessions. A gun (which like other frontiersmen of that day he passionately and personally loved), an ax (with which he could perform almost any feat), the clothes he stood in, the tools of his wildwoods profession, and the world before him, full, intoxicatingly full of untrodden paths leading into bright enticing danger. Prosperity? A home of his own? Above all, regular work? Never, as long as there were squirrels and deer to shoot and logs to make temporary shelters withal!

His roamings took him into Ohio, the early river and lake settlements of which were at that time horribly marshy and fever-ridden. There he encountered the lure which brings most young adventurers in under a roof and beside a hearth-fire. He fell in love. A pretty Vermont girl was visiting some cousins there and had set up a little millinery shop, where she made and sold the scoop-bonnets of the period. Do you see them, the tall, big-boned surveyor, with his magnetic personality, pungent with the odor of freedom, and the pink-cheeked, white-fingered little amateur milliner?

She went back to Vermont to her family, and he followed her. I have often amused myself by walking around over the roads and paths and fields he must have trod during his wooing, and trying to imagine his impatience of the cribbed and cabined superfluity and conventionality of the Vermont life, which looked so primitive and bare to my other grandfather.

He endured it for some months, till his wooing was successful, and, just after her twenty-first birthday, the gentle, home-loving girl put her hand upon his sinewy arm and followed him out into the wilds. This was in 1838 when the wilds were very wild indeed. My great-uncle, who was her little brother at that time conceived a lifelong admiration and affection for the great, strapping, warm-hearted hero who came to take away his big sister. He used to tell me stories of that impetuous wooing, and of the strange impression left on the deeply-rooted mountain-people by the meteor-like appearance and disappearance of this startling, unreliable, dangerously alive personality, living so immorally free from all the rules and possessions and standards which bore them down to the earth, and to which they so tenaciously clung. My great-uncle always ended these stories of his brother-in-law (whom he never saw but on that occasion) by saying, "He was a talented man, with a powerful personality, who could have done anything he chose." He also told me, "Our minister said of Albert that he was a wild, free son of Nature." I take it the minister had had some contact with the romantic-school phraseology so much in fashion at that date.

It was a bitterly hard life which the Vermont girl had chosen, full of extravagant hardships and privations of which she could never have dreamed. They lived here and there, always from hand to mouth, always as far beyond the edge of the settlements as it was possible to take a family of young children, for they had five little girls by the time they had been married a decade. Once or twice her husband made an attempt to enter regular life, to run a store in a frontier settlement, to take an everyday job; but these trials never lasted long, and their old life was taken up, log-cabin after log-cabin, rough clearings

in the primeval forest, days when there was nothing
but corn-meal in the pantry, long treks in covered
wagons to escape from the fever-and-ague which
burned and ravaged them; never more possessions
than could be drawn by a team of lean horses, . . .
and always unbroken love and devotion between the
two wayfarers. Wherever their caravan halted for
a few months was home to the woodsman's wife,
because he was there; his vitality, his free-hearted
zest in whatever came to them, bore her along like
a tidal wave. And to the end of her days she wor-
shipped the memory of his deep, never-wavering
passion for her.

You can imagine that her comfortably well-to-do
family thought he took a very queer way to show it,
and with Yankee out-spokenness told them both so,
as cuttingly as Yankee tongues can speak. Without
a hesitation she flung her family ties away along
with her love of home, her woman's love for stability,
her mother's anxiety about her little girls. Not till
long after his death did she again resume relations
with her family.

Her little girls, never having known any other life,
saw nothing unusual in the one they led, especially
as their mother, her personality doubled and trebled
by the exigencies of her life, stood, somehow, miracu-

lously between them and the most impossible of the
hardships to which their father so light-heartedly
condemned them. They were always dressed in well-
mended garments, they had shoes and stockings,
they were clean and cherished, there was always
cheer and loving-kindness between their father and
mother, and when there was only corn-meal mush
for supper, they scarcely noticed it, because of the
old songs and stories of which their mother had such
a store. My mother sang them to me, and I now
sing them to my children, those old folk-songs with
which my grandmother charmed away hunger from
her little children. They adored their great, rol-
licking father, always in high spirits, and they pre-
ferred the deer-steaks and squirrel stews which were
the results of his wonderful marksmanship, to the
tough, stringy beef and salt pork which was the diet
of the other frontier children. One of my mother's
vivid recollections is of looking out of the window
on a snowy day and seeing her stalwart father
emerge from the woods into the clearing, carrying
. . . a very Robin Hood . . . a whole deer's car-
cass on his broad shoulders. He cast it down before the door and called, like a great boy, for his
women-folk to come and admire him! She says she
can close her eyes now, see the blood ruddy on the

snow, and her father's thrown-back head and bright, laughing face.

Of course, when the news of gold in California came, burning-hot like wild-fire from the west, he was one of the first to go. He would be. A distant, uncertain, and dangerous expedition, into unknown country; could he resist such an alluring combination? Of course, he could have resisted it if he had tried; but he did not try. He never tried.

Also, of course, it was really out of the question to transport a wife and five little girls across an untracked continent, full of Indians. He was to go alone, make a brief stay, get the lay of the land, and come back, his pockets full of gold, to take the family out in a ship around the Horn. It was all settled in his mind as if the gold were heavy in his pockets. The separation would be short . . . he was sure of it, as he was always sure of whatever would ensure his being free of the slightest constraint. . . . He moved his family into the nearest settlement, cashed in on everything saleable, added a small sum that had just come to him as his share of his father's small property, and got together enough to support his family for a year. It took little enough, as they had always lived. And he would be back before the year was out, rolling in gold.

With empty pockets and a high heart he took his gun and his ax, kissed his family good-by and went away planning to live off the country as he traveled, as he always had.

One letter came back from California, the only one he ever wrote, since he had never before been separated from the one human being he had loved. He had had a gloriously adventurous time in getting out there, Indians, drought, snow, heat, grizzly bears —all the regulation accompaniments of the transcontinental trip in 1849. He struck it rich at once, and as one of the first on the ground had a wonderful claim of his own. They would all be rich in no time.

In no time he was dead.

For an interminable period his wife heard nothing, and then, very vaguely, that he had died of "mountain fever." He had been dead and buried for months before she learned that she was a widow at thirty-two with five helpless little girls and not a penny in the world.

OCTOBER, 1918

MORNING

I was crossing the Place de la Concorde, and stopped for an instant, fascinated by the sinister expression of an immense cannon, painted in serpentine streaks and stripes, the muzzle of its tube distorted by an explosion so that a twisted flap of steel hung down like a broken jaw-bone. A hail made me turn around. The elegant old man who was an American correspondent for a New York newspaper, came up with an expression of approval. "Magnificent display, isn't it?" he said, waving his hand towards the ranks of captured cannon and mitrailleuses, standing thick on the public square. "Why didn't you bring your children?"

The gulf between his generation and mine yawned deep. I told myself the part of wisdom was to close my lips on what I felt. But the cannon leered at me too insolently, with its torn muzzle.

I answered, "I'm glad enough when the police seem to be getting the better of a band of ruffians who've been terrorizing the town. But I don't take the children to see the bloody clubs with which . . ."

"Oh, come!" said my old friend, genially. "Feminine emotionality! These don't look much like bloody clubs. They look more like part of a steel-foundry."

"Every cannon here is wreathed in human viscera, spattered with human brains, and stands in a pool of human blood, if we only had eyes to see!" I said moderately.

"Why, you talk like a pacifist!" said the old gentleman, forgetting his usual politeness to women.

"I thought the unforgivable sin of the Germans was in forcing a war on a world that has outgrown war! If war is so hateful a thing, why complacently lay out to view its hideous instruments of torture?"

"Because," said my old friend with deep emotion, "because they have been instruments of righteousness!" (For the moment he had forgotten the nationality of the cannon about us.)

"Have they?" I asked. "They're German cannon, remember." In spite of my feeling sick, I could not but laugh at the change in his expression. I went on, "Well, even if they had been sacred Allied cannon, they'd be instruments of torture all the same. I thought we were fighting to put such things on the scrap heap. Why don't we have the decency to hide them from view? We don't put the offal from our slaughter-houses on public view."

"Vegetarianism, next?"

"Oh, no, I eat beefsteaks. But I don't take the children to see the steers killed."

"Of course, I know," said my old friend tolerantly, "that women have a traditional right to be illogical, but *really*. . . . Did you, or did you not turn your personal life upside down to do your share in this war? It would give me brain fever to feel two different ways about the same thing."

"See here," I put it to him, "a man, crazy-drunk comes roaring down our street. Who *wouldn't* feel two ways about him? I certainly do. First, I know that society has been wrongly organized to permit any boy to grow up crazed with whiskey; and second, I know that my children must be protected, now, at this very minute. Shooting that man dead isn't going to help the general situation at all. If we are not to have a perpetual procession of crazy-drunk men coming down our street (*and our own men among them*) we must change the organization of society by long, patient, and constructive efforts. In the meantime with the drunken man pounding on my door, if the police don't do what is necessary, why, of course, I will throw a dishpan of scalding water down on him. But I wouldn't spend the rest of my life making speeches about the dishpan."

My sophisticated old friend had for me the smiling amusement one feels for a bright child talking about what he does not understand. Taking up the sharp ax of Ecclesiastes, he struck a great blow at the root of the matter, "No, my dear girl, no, you don't. A well-meaning, high-principled woman like you, can do a great deal, but she cannot amputate a vital part of human nature. You can't make manly, brave men ashamed of war and it's a lucky thing for you you can't, for if you did, there would be nobody to stand between you and the bullies. Take it from a man nearly twice your age, that without the soldier in every man (and that means love of force and submission to force—you must swallow that!) there would be no order in the world. You needn't try to reduce that element of force to mere business-like police-work. It can't be done. There would be anarchy in the twinkling of an eye. You won't believe this, because it doesn't fit into your womanish, preconceived notions. But it doesn't make any difference whether you believe it or not. Such are the facts. And all your noble phrases can't change them."

I turned and left him. I did not believe a word
he said, of course . . . but. . . . There *is* a horrible side to human nature. . . . Suppose that to
hold it in check it might be necessary . . .

AFTERNOON

"Oh, mother, this is Thursday and the merry-go-
round in the Parc of the Château is running.
Couldn't you take us?"

We set off, the three of us, hand in hand, crossed
the arid, bare Place d'Armes where the great Louis
had mustered his troops, hobbled up over the villain-
ous paving-stones of the gray entrance court and
came by beautiful leafy avenues to where the primitive circle of wooden horses whirled slowly about, as
a one-armed soldier turned the crank. I was left on
a bench, with the other waiting mothers, watching
our children's pleasure.

My two were at once in another world—Jimmy's
a mere wide world of enchantment, as befitted his
five-year-old ignorance. He swam through the air,
a vague smile of beatitude on his lips. Sally sat
very straight, one hand on her hip, the other
stretched out in a gesture of command. She was
perhaps Charlemagne before the defeated Saxons,

or possibly Joan of Arc at Orleans. Sally's class at school begins to have some notions of history.

When the crippled soldier was tired, and we had paid our copper sous, we wandered on, to a bench in front of a statue of mellow marble. Here I sat down while the children ran about, shouting and kicking up the chestnut leaves which laid a carpet of cloth-of-gold under their feet. Their laughter sounded distant in my ears. I was hearing again the cock-sure old voice of the morning. . . . "Anarchy in a moment if respect for force were eliminated . . . you cannot amputate a part of human nature . . ."

What was my little daughter saying, with her amusing older-sister air of omniscience? "Did you know, Jimmy, that it was a king who had all this made, out of nothing at all. We've just had that in school. It was only a bare, sandy plain, and he had all the trees brought here, and the terraces made, and the water brought here. . . . It cost millions and millions."

Jimmy looked up in astonishment at the giant oak over him. "Can you carry great big trees like these around with you?" he asked.

"No, gracious, no! It was ever so long ago.

They've grown up since. They were just scrawny little saplings. They've got an old picture at school that shows how it was when he was alive. Awfully ugly!"

"I wouldn't have liked it then," said Jimmy.

Sally hooted at his ignorance. "My goodness, you don't suppose you'd ever have got any chance to play here if you'd lived then. Not much! We never could have got in. They had soldiers at all the gates to keep people out."

Jimmy's sense of the probable was outraged. There were some things too tall to be believed, even if Sally did say them. "What was it *for*, if nobody was allowed in?"

"It was for the king. Everything was for the king then. And he only let in his own family and his special friends."

"I should think people would ha' been mad to see the king hogging everything for himself," Jimmy said vigorously.

"Oh, they were used to it," explained Sally. "They thought it had to be that way. All the learned men in those days told them that everything would go to pieces and everybody would rob and murder everybody else if they didn't have a king and think they loved him more than anybody else."

Once more Jimmy's sense of the probable rose up to protest, "They didn't *love* that old hog-it-all king!" The little twentieth-century American brain refused to credit this ridiculous and inherently impossible idea.

(. . . and yet how many generations of men suffered and died to affirm that idea as the natural and inevitable foundation of society!)

"Well, they thought they had to, and so they thought they did," said Sally lucidly. "The way we love our governments now. But after a couple of hundred years or so they found out the learned men didn't know so much, and that it wasn't having a king that kept folks from robbing and murdering all the time. So they got together and came out here from Paris and took all this away from him. And that's how we get in to play."

Jimmy's fancy was tickled by a new idea. "I bet he'd be surprised if he could see us playing here."

Sally dramatized the scene, instantly. "Wouldn't he though! Suppose he should come walking right down those marble steps with his high wig and his big-buckled shoes, and his clothes all solid gold and diamonds, and suppose he should walk right up to us and say, "You good-for-nothing common-people, what are you doing in MY park? I'll have you boiled in oil at once!"

Jimmy was a little intimidated. He took his big sister's hand and said in rather a small voice, "What would you say back?"

Sally made a dramatic gesture of scorn. "I'd say, 'Get away from here, you old King. Don't you know you're dead?' And then, Jimmy, you know ghosts aren't solid. I'd just draw off and run right through him, gold clothes and diamonds and all, like this."

She executed a headlong assault on space and came back laughing.

Jimmy, reassured, caught the note, "Yes," he said swaggering, "I would too, I'd say, 'You old King, you're dead!' and I'd run right through him too."

It was the most delightful of all the games Sally had invented. They went at it with gusto, their faces rosy and laughing as they took turns in dashing through the non-existent might, majesty, and glory of a dead idea.

It was a game which amused their mother quite as much as the children. I sat watching them at it, till it was time to start home back through the rich magnificence of the old park which had been planted for a king's pleasure and which throughout the silent, purposeful centuries had grown to beauty for the people.

A BRETON AMONG HSÜ HSI

THE black-and-white maid told me I was expected
and showed me into the drawing-room to wait. As
I waited I looked around at the beautiful room with
the leaden depression which such beautiful rooms
always produce in me. It was a wonderfully elabo-
rate composition with as many details in it as there
are notes on a page of music, and every one of them
was correct and accredited. As I stepped in through
the door the whole shouted in my ears a pæan of
religiously devout acceptance of the fashion then
prevailing in interior decoration.

The floor was dully lustrous, avoiding the vulgar
shininess of varnish so esteemed a decade or so before. There was a great deal of black in all the
fabrics as was then the fashion (now it would be ver-
milion and verdigris green); chintz curtains with a
black background and a splashingly-colored design
of wreaths and strange large birds; black satin sofa-
pillows, with stiff quilled ruffles in brilliant colors
to match the birds. The shades of the electric lights
(which were of course designed to make them look
like candles) were ornamented with cut-out black

silhouettes of nude ladies with extremely long legs. The furniture was either all "antique" or had been doctored to look as though it were. A large, dark, carved chest stood against a wall—to contain what it was difficult to conjecture. The chairs had the correct kind of legs and backs and arms, that is, the kind that had not yet been copied sufficiently to spoil it for the discerning taste; and the straight, curiously-shaped table was at least two jumps ahead of anything shown at that time even by the most enterprising department-store. The walls, in accordance with the order of the day, were for the most part smartly and knowingly bare, with a few permissible reproductions of Chinese landscapes; one a tall, narrow study of bamboo shoots, another a long, narrow study of snowy mountains, depicted in three or four lines (this year it would be, I suppose, an 1858 panel by Jolly).

I sat down in what looked like the most comfortable of the distinguished chairs, my feet on one of the correctly Oriental rugs, and looked dispiritedly about me for some sign of living taste in all that tastefully arranged room. There was plenty of taste shown there; but it smelled so of the pages of an expensive magazine printed on highly-glazed paper, that presently, as I sat there, despairing of my race,

I felt my own body take on the same flat, two-dimensional unreality. Well, that is the sort of flat and unreal creatures human beings are when it comes to taste, I reflected.

There was not, so far as I could see, one single object in that room (and God knows there were plenty of objects in it!) which rang out with the clear, brave note of a thing chosen because it gives pleasure. Everything about me wore a large, invisible but plainly legible placard, setting forth that it was there because it was "the thing"; and that the instant "the thing" was something else it would be cast out and replaced with something else as meaningless as itself in the life of the owner.

The whole expensive show was perched on the branch of other people's opinions, and was ready to fall to the ground as soon as that branch waved in the wind of a new fashion. There was not one object which suggested what you might think would be the first, simple, hearty, healthy instinct of prospering humanity, the desire to surround itself with what it likes. No, in its abject consistency, the room shamelessly proclaimed that its ambition was to be well thought of by "people in the know" and not at all to please the family who had paid for it and had to live with it.

Docility in human beings is always a dreadful quality, but docility in matters of taste is shameful. I sighed, and fixed my eyes on what looked like a Chardin. Oh, yes, Chardin was "in" now, I remembered. But an ordinary private family would be as little likely to own a real Chardin as a real Veermeer. I reflected that as soon as it was discovered not to be a genuine one, it would certainly be sent off to the junk shop. And yet it was a delightful canvas, apparently by some one of the period who had absorbed Chardin's atmosphere and loved it as we do. If it looked so much like a Chardin that only the X-ray could tell the difference, why wasn't it as good as a Chardin? I fell into a meditation on the hideous ways of collectors of pictures, blasphemers against the Holy Ghost of Art that they are. Ostensibly they buy pictures because they love good paintings (I am not referring to art *dealers!*). A collector sees a small canvas, said to be a Teniers, and is ready to pay a fantastic price for it, enough to endow a school for all time. Some expert with a chemical test proves that it is not a Teniers. It is the same picture as before, the very same; but now the lover of good art would not hang it on his walls, if it were given to him.

What kind of a race is that to belong to, I asked

myself plaintively. They don't want beauty, they don't want art, they haven't even the plain courage that any dog or monkey has, to want what they want. They want what other people pretend to want.

I got up restlessly, crossed over to the other side of the room, turned my eyes to the side I had left, and was electrified. There in the center of the wall, next to a small reproduction of a Madhu camel-fight, was a large canvas, a solidly painted, honest, dark, sentimental Jules Breton. I gazed at it with profound thankfulness. There was not an extenuating circumstance. It was his usual peasant girl, done with his usual psuedo-realism, with her usual bare feet, every muddy toe conscientiously drawn, and it had darkened to the usual Breton gloom. It swore at the top of its voice at all the knowing, Orientalized, simplified, subtle things about it, and my heart leaped up to hear it swear. For it sounded like a living voice.

Here was something that must have been bought some time ago (for nobody can actually have bought a Breton recently), which must have been hung on the wall when Bretons were in style. But it had not been banished when the style had changed!

And yet the rest of the room told me unmistakably that the owner of that room knew as well as any one else what was now thought of that Breton by people "in the know."

Well, there was one visitor who appreciated it. Never before had I thought to admire so ardently the dull, faithful, unimaginative surface of a Breton. But I gazed at it with affection. There could be no reason for its presence except that somebody liked it enough to keep it in spite of what other people thought. Well, now—I took heart—maybe the situation wasn't so desperate as I had thought. Perhaps we may have a live national taste in art, twenty or more generations later on. If there was *any*body not an artist himself, who had the honesty and courage which must be at the foundation of anything alive in artistic taste, why perhaps . . .

Just then a dreadful possibility came into my mind—perhaps it had been a wedding present from a wealthy uncle not to be offended?

On this my host and hostess came in. As we talked of the object of my visit (which had nothing to do with art) I was constantly spying on the expression of their eyes, listening half-hopefully, half-despairingly to the sound of their voices, watching feverishly every turn of expression in their kind, honest faces. I had never seen them before that day and probably shall have no occasion to see them again. But I often think of them and wonder about them. They really looked as though they might be capable of not being ashamed to like a picture no longer in fashion. Perhaps they *had* kept that Breton on their walls out of sheer, honest, brave, artistic integrity. . . .

But the more I think of it, the more unlikely it seems.

ALMERA HAWLEY CANFIELD
b. 1787; m. 1808; d. 1874

Of course I never saw her. She died years before I was born. But she left behind her a portrait so full of her personality that no living figure is more human to me than my great-grandmother.

I do not at all refer to the portrait over the dining-room mantelpiece, showing her as a withered old woman in a frilled cap, which is now the only tangible sign of her existence left in her old home. No; that might have been any withered old woman in a frilled cap.

There is another portrait of my great-grandmother not done on canvas with oils. Here are some of the strokes which one by one, at long intervals, as if casually and by chance, have painted it for me.

When I was about eight years old, I went out one day to watch old Lemuel Hager, who came once a year to mow the grass in the orchard back of the house. As he clinked the whetstone over the ringing steel of his scythe, he looked down at me and remarked: "You favor the Hawley side of the family, don't you? There's a look around your mouth sort o' like Aunt Almera, your grandmother —no—my sakes, you must be her great-granddaughter! Wa'l—think of that! And it don't seem more'n yesterday I saw her come stepping out same's you did just now; not so much bigger'n you are this minute, for all she must have been sixty years old then. She always was the *littlest* woman. But for all that she marched up to me, great lummox of a boy, and she said, 'Is it true, what I hear folks say, Lemuel, that you somehow got out of school without having learned how to read?' And I says, 'Why, Mis Canfield, to tell the truth, I never did seem to git the hang of books, and I never could seem to git up no sort of interest in 'em.'

"And she says back, 'Well, no great boy of eighteen in the town *I* live in is a-goin' to grow up without he knows how to read the Declaration of Independence,' says she. And she made me stop work for an hour—she paid me just the same for it—took me into the house, and started teaching me.

"Great land of love! if the teacher at school had 'a' taught me like that, I'd 'a' been a minister! I felt as though she'd cracked a hole in my head and

was just pouring the l'arning in through a funnel.
And 'twa'n't more'n ten minutes before she found
out 'twas my eyes the trouble. I'm terrible near-
sighted. Well, that was before the days when everybody wore specs. There wa'n't no way to git specs
for me; but you couldn't stump Aunt Almera. She
just grabbed up a sort of magnifying-glass that she
used, she said, for her sewing, now her eyes were
kind o' failing her, and she give it to me. 'I'll take
bigger stitches,' says she, laughing; 'big stitches
don't matter so much as reading for an American
citizen.'

"Well, sir, she didn't forgit me; she kept at me to
practice to home with my magnifying-glass, and it
was years before I could git by the house without
Aunt Almera come out on the porch and hollered to
me, that bossy way she had, 'Lemuel, you come in
for a minute and let me hear you read.' Sometimes
it kind o' madded me, she had such a way o' thinkin'
she could make everybody stand 'round. And sometimes it made me laugh, she was so old, and not much
bigger'n my fist. But, by gol, I l'arned to read, and
I have taken a sight of comfort out of it. I don't
never set down in the evening and open up the
Necronsett 'Journal' without I think of Aunt Almera
Canfield."

One day I was sent over to Mrs. Pratt's to get some butter, and found it just out of the churn. So I sat down to wait till Mrs. Pratt should work it over, munching on a cookie, and listening to her stream of talk—the chickens, the hail-storm of the other day, had my folks begun to make currant jelly yet? and so on—till she had finished and was shaping the butter into beautiful round pats. "This always puts me in mind of Aunt Almera," she said, interrupting an account of how the men had chased a woodchuck up a *tree*—who ever heard of such a thing? "Whenever I begin to make the pats, I remember when I was a girl working for her. She kept you right up to the mark, I tell you, and you ought to have seen how she lit into me when she found out some of my butter-pats were just a little over a pound and some a little less. It was when she happened to have too much cream and she was 'trading in' the butter at the store. You'd have thought I'd stolen a fifty-cent piece to hear her go on! 'I sell those for a pound; they've got to *be* a pound,' says she, the way she always spoke, as though that ended it.

" 'But land sakes, Mis' Canfield,' says I, all out o' patience with her, 'an ounce or two one way or the other—it's as likely to be more as less, you know!

What difference does it make? *Nobody* expects to make their pats just a pound! How could you?'

" 'How could you? How could you?' says she. 'Why, just the way you make anything else the way it ought to be—by keeping at it till it *is* right. What other way is there?'

"I didn't think you could do it. I *knew* you couldn't; but you always had to do the way Mis Canfield said, and so I began grumbling under my breath about high-handed, fussy old women. But she never minded what you *said* about her, so long as you did your work right. So I fussed and fussed, clipping off a little, and adding on a little, and weighing it between times. It was the awfulest bother you ever saw, because it spoiled the shape of your pat to cut at it so much, and you had to start it over again every time.

"Well, you wouldn't believe it, how soon I got the hang of it! She'd made me think about it so much, I got interested, and it wasn't any time at all before I could tell the heft of a pat to within a fraction of an ounce just by the feel of it in my hand. And I never forgot it. You never do forget that kind of thing. I brought up my whole family on that story. 'Now you do that spelling lesson just exactly *right*,' I'd say to my Lucy, 'just the way Aunt Almera made me do the butter pats!'"

I was sitting on the steps of the Town Hall, trying to make a willow whistle, when the janitor came along and opened the door. "The Ladies' Aid are going to have a supper in the downstairs room," he explained, getting out a broom. I wandered in to visit with him while he swept and dusted the pleasant little community sitting-room where our village social gatherings were held. He moved an armchair and wiped off the frame of the big portrait of Lincoln. "Your great-grandmother gave that, do you know it?" he observed, and then, resting on the broom for a moment and beginning to laugh, "Did you ever hear how Aunt Almera got folks stirred up to do something about this room? Well, 'twas so *like* her! The place used to be the awfulest hole you ever saw. Years ago they'd used it to lock up drunks in, or anybody that had to be locked up. Then after the new jail was built the sheriff began to take prisoners down there. But nobody did anything to this room to clean it up or fix it. It belongs to the town, you know, and nobody ever'll do anything that they think they can put off on the town. The women used to talk a lot about it—what a nice

place 'twould be for socials, and how 'twould keep
the boys off the streets, and how they could have
chicken suppers here, same as other towns, if this
room was fixed up. But whose business was it to
fix it up? The town's of course! And of course
nobody ever thinks that he and his folks are all there
is *to* the town. No, they just jawed about it, and
kept saying 'wa'n't the selectmen shiftless because
they didn't see to it!' But of course the selectmen
didn't have the money to do anything. Nothing in
the law about using tax money to fix up rooms for
sociables, is there? And those were awful tight
times, when money came hard and every cent of
tax money had to be put to some good plain use.
So the selectmen said *they* couldn't do anything.
And nobody else would, because it wasn't anybody's
business in particular, and nobody wanted to be put
upon and made to do more than his share. And the
room got dirtier and dirtier, with the lousy old mattress the last drunk had slept on right there on the
floor in the corner, and broken chairs and old wooden
boxes, and dust and dry leaves that had blown in
through the windows when the panes of glass were
broken—regular dumping-ground for trash.

"Well, one morning bright and early—I've heard
my mother tell about it a thousand times—the first

person that went by the Town Hall seen the door open and an awful rattling going on. He peeked in, and there was little old Aunt Almera, in a big gingham apron, her white hair sticking out from underneath a towel she'd tied her head up in, cleaning away to beat the band. She looked up, saw him standing and gaping at her, and says, just as though that was what she did every day for a living, 'Good morning,' she says. 'Nice weather, isn't it?'

"He went away kind of quick, and told about her over in the store, and they looked out, and sure enough out she come, limping along (she had the rheumatism *bad*) and dragging that old mattress with her. She drug it out in front to a bare place, and poured some kerosene on it and set fire to it; and I guess by that time every family in the street was looking out at her from behind the window-shades. Then she went back in, leaving it there burning up, high and smoky, and in a minute out she came again with her dustpan full of trash. She flung that on the fire as if she'd been waiting all her life to have the chance to get it burned up, and went back for more. And there she was, bobbing back and forth all the fore part of the morning. Folks from the Lower Street that hadn't heard about it would come up for their mail, and just stop dead,

to see the bonfire blazing and Aunt Almera limping
out with maybe an old broken box full of junk in her
arms. She'd always speak up just as pleasant and
gentle to them—*that* made 'em feel queerer than
anything else. Aunt Almera talking so mild! 'Well,
folks, how are you this morning?' she'd say. 'And
how are all the folks at home?' And then *slosh!*
would go a pail of dirty water, for as soon as she
got it swept out, didn't she get down on her creaking
old marrow-bones and scrub the floor! All that afternoon every time anybody looked out, splash!
there'd be Aunt Almera throwing away the water
she'd been scrubbing the floor with. Folks felt about
as big as a pint-cup by that time, but nobody could
think of anything to do or say, for fear of what
Aunt Almera might say back at them, and everybody was always kind o' slow about trying to stop
her once she got started on anything. So they just
kept indoors and looked at each other like born
fools, till Aunt Almera crawled back home. It
mighty nigh killed her, that day's work. She was all
crippled up for a fortnight afterwards with rheumatism. But you'd better believe folks stirred around
those two weeks, and when she was out and around
again there was this room all fixed up just the way
'tis now, with furniture, and the floor painted, and

white curtains to the windows, and all. Nobody
said a word to her about it, and neither did she say
a word when she saw it—she never was one to do
any crowing over folks—once she'd got her own
way."

The hassocks in our pew began to look shabby,
and my aunt brought them home from church to
put fresh carpeting on them. They suggested
church, of course, and as she worked on them a great
many reminiscences came to her mind. Here is one:
"I used to love to ride horseback, and grandmother
always made father let me, although he was afraid
to have me. Well, one summer evening, right after
supper I went for a little ride, and didn't get home
till about half-past seven. As I rode into the yard
I looked through the open windows, and there was
grandmother putting her bonnet on; and it came to
me in a flash that I'd promised to go to evening
prayers with her. I was a grown-up young lady
then, but I was scared! You did what you'd promised grandmother you would, or something happened. So I just fell off my horse, turned him out
in the night pasture, saddle and all, and ran into the
house. Grandmother was putting on her gloves, and,
although she saw me with my great looped-up riding

skirt on and my whip in my hand, she never said a
word nor lifted an eyebrow; just went on wetting
her fingers and pushing the gloves down on them as
though I was ready with my best hat on.   That
scared me worse than ever.   I tore into my room,
slipped off my skirt, put on another right over my
riding trousers, slammed on a hat, threw a long cape
around me, and grabbed my gloves.   As the last bell
began to ring and grandmother stepped out of the
house, I stepped out beside her, all right as to the
outer layer, but with the perspiration streaming down
my face.   I'd hurried so, and those great thick riding
trousers were so hot under my woolen skirt!   My!
I thought I'd die!   And it was worse in the church!
Over in our dark, close corner pew there wasn't a
breath of air.   It must have been a hundred by the
thermometer.   I was so hot I just had to do something or die!   There weren't but a few people in the
church, and nobody anywhere near our corner, and
it was as dark as could be, back in our high pew.   So
when we knelt down for the General Confession I
gathered the cape all around me, reached up under
my full skirt, unbuttoned those awful riding trousers,
and just cautiously slipped them off.   My!   What
a relief it was!   Grandmother felt me rustling around
and looked over sharp at me, to see what I was

doing. When she saw the riding trousers, she looked shocked, and frowned; but I guess I must have looked terribly hot and red, so she didn't say anything.

"Well, I knew it was an awful thing to do in church, and I was so afraid maybe somebody *had* seen me, although old Dr. Skinner, the rector, was the only one high enough up to look over the pew-top, and he was looking at his Prayer Book. But I felt as mean as though he'd been looking right at me. Well, he finally got through the prayers and began on the First Lesson. It was something out of the Old Testament, that part about how the Jews went back and repaired the broken walls of Jerusalem, each one taking a broken place for his special job, and then how they got scared away, all but a few, from the holes in the walls they were trying to fix up. Dr. Skinner always read the Lessons very loud and solemn, as though he were reading them right at somebody, and he'd sort of turn from one to another in the congregation with his forefinger pointed at them, as if he meant that just for them. What *do* you suppose I felt like when he turned right towards our corner and leaned 'way over and shook his finger at me, and said in a loud, blaming tone, 'But Asher continued and *abode* in *his* breaches!' I gave a little gasp, and grandmother turned towards me quick. When she saw the expression on my face (I guess I must have looked funny), she just burst right out into that great laugh of hers—ha! ha! ha! She laughed so she couldn't stop, and had to actually get up and go out of church, her handkerchief stuffed into her mouth. We could hear her laughing as she went down the walk outside!

"You'd have thought she'd be mortified, wouldn't you? *I* was mortified almost to death! But she wasn't a bit. She laughed every time she thought of it, for years after that. It was just like her! She did love a good laugh! Let anything happen that struck her as funny, and she'd laugh, no *matter* what!"

Later on, as we carried the hassocks back to the church and put them in our pew, my aunt said, reflectively, looking round the empty church: "I never come in here that I don't remember how grandmother used to say the Creed, loud and strong—she always spoke up so clear: 'From thence he shall come to judge the quick and the dead. I believe in the Holy Ghost: The Holy Catholic Church: The Communion of Saints: The Forgiveness of sins—' and then she'd stop dead, while everybody went on,

'The Resurrection of the body;' and then she'd chime in again, 'And the Life everlasting, Amen.' You couldn't help noticing it, she took the greatest pains you should. But if anybody said anything about it she always said that she didn't believe in the resurrection of the body, and she wasn't going to *say* she did. Sometimes the ministers would get wrought up, especially the young ones, and one of them went to the bishop about it, but nobody ever did anything. What *could* you do? And grandmother went right on saying the Creed that way to the day of her death."

On the hundredth anniversary of the organization of our parish there were, of course, great doings in the way of centenary celebrations. Many of the old rectors came back to visit, and to make after-dinner talks and to preach at special services. One of the most interesting of these old men was the Reverend Mr. Jason Gillett, who had been rector for a year shortly after the Civil War, when he was a young man just out of the Theological Seminary. He had since become well-known, one might say famous (in church circles at least) for his sermons of a fervor truly evangelical (so it was said), delivered in a voice noted for its harmony and moving qualities. We had often read about his preaching, in the Church papers. He had brought up from decay several old parishes and had founded one of the finest and most thriving in Chicago.

There was a stir when his return for a day was announced, and the morning when he preached, the church was crowded to the doors. He proved to be a spiritual-faced, white-haired, handsome old man, equipped with fine eyes and beautiful hands as well as his famous voice. He preached a sermon which held every one in the church breathlessly attentive. I noticed that his stole was exquisitely worked in gold thread, and after the service, when the Altar Guild were putting things away, we saw that his surplice was of extremely fine material, with a deep band of embroidery about the hem. "Loving lady-parishioners," conjectured one of the Guild, holding it up.

"They say the women are always crazy about him, everywhere, and no wonder!" said another. "Such a fascinating, attractive personality."

"How did you like his sermon?" I asked. Personally I had found it rather too dramatic for my taste. It rubs me the wrong way when I feel that somebody is trying to work my feelings up, although I always feel a little ashamed of this natural ungraciousness, which is labeled in the talk of the old people of our locality as "Canfield cussedness."

One of my companions answered me, "Why, the tears ran right down my cheeks, towards the end of that sermon!"

And another added, "Such a power for good as he has been, all his life. Think of his having begun his wonderful work right here in our little parish."

The door opened and the preacher himself entered in his black cassock, followed by a group of people. He was a little flushed from the handshaking reception he had been holding in the vestibule and still wore the affable smile which had gone with the handshaking. The men and women who had followed him in were still talking two or three at once, trying to get his attention, still fixing their eyes on him, unwilling to leave him, moved evidently by his mere presence.

"It's a renewal of my youth to be here again in this dear old parish," he said genially, using a set of inflections of his fine voice quite different from those of the sermon, "I find it all comes back to me with the utmost freshness. Ah, youth! Youth!"

He broke off to say in still another tone, "I know

none of you will object to my saying also that it is
an immense relief to find the parish rid of that de-
testable incubus Mrs. Almera Canfield. You must
all breathe a happier air, since she took her mock-
ing cynicism into another world."

A quick shifting of eyes, lifted eyebrows, and suppressed smiles told him that he had been indiscreet.
He faced the uncomfortable little situation with a
well-oiled ease of manner. "Have I offended some
one here?" he asked, instantly, turning towards us.
Then, seeing by my expression that I was the one
involved, he said gallantly, "It's not possible that
so very young a lady can have any connection with
a generation so long since passed away."

"Mrs. Almera Canfield was my great-grandmother," I said, perhaps rather drily. Not that I
cared especially about Great-grandmother, of whom
at that time I knew very little, and who seemed as
remote from my life as Moses. But that same hateful, contrary streak in my nature was roused to re-
sentment by his apparent assumption that a smile and
a word from him could set anything straight.

He found the fact of my relationship and of my
knowledge of it very amusing, "Where, oh, where,
out of Vermont could you find a modern young
person who even knew the name of her great-grand-

mother? I'm sure, my dear, that family loyalties are outlawed by such a long interval of years. And I'm also sure by one look at you, that you are not at all like your great-grandmother."

He seemed to think, I reflected, that I would be sure to take that as a compliment. She must have been an old Tartar.

I could think of nothing to answer, and he turned away again, to go on chatting with the people who continued to hang on his words, laughing loudly when he said something playful, nodding a grave concurrence in his more seriously expressed opinions, their eyes always fixed on his.

They all moved away, out into the church and down the aisle and I did not see him again till that evening, when, quite unexpectedly, he appeared beside me in the break-up of the company after the large public dinner.

"I feel that I owe you an apology," he began persuasively and courteously, "for having let slip that chance remark about a relative of yours, even so very far distant. I would not have said it, of course, if I had dreamed that any member of her family . . ."
Up to this point he had used the same sort of voice and tone that he had employed after church that morning, but now he suddenly dropped into another

tone, quite different. I had a divination that it was not only quite different from any inflection he had used, but also not at all what he had had the intention of using. "I try to be fair . . . to be tolerant . . . to be *forgiving*, but really I can never forget the . . ." (it was as if a wave of lava had burst up out of the smiling pleasantness of his agreeable manner) "I simply can't express to you the blighting, devastating effect she had on me, young, sensitive, emotional and ardent as I was at that time!"

He started at the violence of his own voice and glanced quickly around him as if to see whether any one else had heard it. And then he looked intensely annoyed by his own gesture.

"You are probably assuming that I refer," he went on more quietly, but still pressingly (it was as if for some reason he quite cared to influence my unimportant opinion), "that I refer to her dictatorial assurance that she knew better than any one else how things ought to be run. Of course you must have heard plenty of stories of her overbearing ways. But that is not the point; no, although she was a hard parishioner on that account for a young clergyman struggling with the administration of his first parish. What came back to me, in a wave of bitterness as I stood up to preach to-day, was the remembrance of the peculiarly corrosive vein of irony, with which she withered and dried to the root any play of poetry or emotion in those about her. So far from feeling any natural, human sympathy with ardent youth, she had a cold intolerance for any nature richer or more warmly colored than her own. She made it her business to drop an acid sneer upon any expression of emotion or any appeal to it; and a life-long practice in that diabolical art had given her a technique of raw, brutal roughness, guaranteed to hamstring any spontaneity of feeling, any warmth of personality. I could quote you dozens of such poisoned shafts of hers. . . . Here's one that came into my mind as I stood again in that pulpit, where I first dedicated myself to the service of God.

"I can never forget her comment on the first sermon in which I let myself go into the fervor which was given me by nature. It was an appeal for foreign missions, a cause always dear to my heart. I was carried away by my feelings, and fairly poured out my soul to my listeners. I have always considered that to be my first real sermon, the first time I felt sure of my Vocation. Afterwards, as I stood in the robing room, faint with the reaction after my emotion, I heard some one just outside the door say, 'Well, Aunt Almera, what did you think of the

sermon?' And what do you think her answer was!
She said, 'Oh, I *like* to see anybody enjoy himself
as much as that young man did.' "

This unexpected conclusion brought to me such
a sudden horrifying desire to laugh that I felt quite
shaken by the necessity to curb it. And it was es-
sential not to let it be seen. For he had wound himself up again to a heat which astonished me. It
was as if he had meant casually to show me an old
scar, and had found to his surprise that the wound
was as raw and smarting as ever.

"Why," he cried, "she all but drove me wholly out
of preaching, at the very outset of my career, sitting there as she did, Sunday after Sunday, fixing
that cynical aged eye on me. You can't know . . .
I hear that you have been brought up, luckily for
you, outside of this deadly New England atmosphere. . . . You can't *imagine* how it kills and
freezes all the warmth and color and fire out of life
to have such a . . . if I hadn't escaped out of it
to . . ."

"I'm afraid I've been brought up mostly in a New
England atmosphere," I said, beginning to feel very
cross and prickly.

As if struck by something in my tone, he now
looked at me very hard. I don't know what he saw

in my face . . . perhaps a family resemblance of
expression . . . but he suddenly seemed to come to
himself with a start. He said abruptly, with an expression of extreme annoyance once more on his
face, "I beg your pardon for bringing all this up. I
can't think what in the world made me!" and turned
away with a noticeable lack of suavity and grace of
manner.

Once I was taken to see an old Irishwoman who
had come from Ireland as a young girl, just after the
great famine in '48, and had gone to work for Great-
grandmother, who was then sixty-three years old.
She told me this story, in her thick, thick early-nine-
teenth-century brogue, which I will not try to re-
produce here: "There was a pretty girl, young and
happy-looking, that lived up the road with her
father, a poor weak rag of a man with a backbone
like a piece of string. He'd married for his second
wife a hard, hard woman. And when they found
out the girl was in trouble, and her sweetheart that
was the cause of it off up in the North Country for
the winter to work as a lumberjack, didn't the step-
mother turn the poor girl out—yes, out like a dog.
And old Mrs. Canfield—that was some kin to you,
I forget what—where I was working, she went right

out and brought her in, and kept her there safe and
sound all winter, treating her as nice as anybody,
letting her sew to pay for her keep, and helping her
make the baby clothes. She'd go with her to church
every Sunday, the girl right on her arm, and nobody
daring to say a word, for fear of old Mrs. Canfield's
tongue, 'For,' she used to say, 'let 'em say a word
if they dare, and I'll tell a few things I know about
some folks in this town who had to be married in a
hurry, and whose babies came into the world ahead
of time.' You see, she was so old she knew everything that had happened from the beginning almost. She'd say, 'There's lots worse things done
every day in this town than anything Margaret's
done,' she'd say, and nobody to answer her back a
word.

"But everybody was thinking it very certain
that the man would never come back, and if he did,
he'd never own the child, nor have anything to do
with Margaret, poor girl! You see, in those days
there weren't any mails that were carried 'way back
off in the woods, and she neither had any word of
him nor he of her. Well, old Mrs. Canfield knew
what people were saying all right, and I could see
that she was troubled in her mind, though she never
lowered her high head by an inch. Margaret's time

drew near, and no sign from John Dawson that was away. But Margaret never lost her faith in him a minute. 'When John is back,' she'd say, just as sure of him as though they'd been married by the priest; but I could see old Mrs. Canfield look queer when she'd hear Margaret talking that way.

"And then one morning, in April 'twas, and we'd all the doors and windows open for the first time, Margaret had gone down the walk to look at the lilac bush to see if there were any buds on it, and around the corner came John Dawson!

"Her back was to him and he hadn't any idea she was there, so when she turned round, they stared at each other for just a minute, as if they'd never seen each other. Now the moment had come, Margaret stood there frozen, just waiting, like a little scared, helpless—I had the half of me hanging out the kitchen window to see what would happen, and I'll never forget it—never—never—never—the look on his face, the astounded look on his face, so full of pity and love, so strong with pity and love. 'Margie! *Margie!*' he said in a loud voice, and threw his sack off his back and his gun from his hand, and ran, ran to take her in his arms.

"Well, when I could see again, I went off to tell old Mrs. Canfield, and there was the old lady in her

own bedroom, standing bolt upright in the middle of
the floor, and crying at the top of her voice. Her
wrinkled old face was just a-sop with tears. Faith,
but it was the grand cry she was having! And the
good it did her! When she came to, she says to me,
'Well,' says she, 'folks aren't so cussed as they seem,
are they?'

"And then we went downstairs to get out the
fruit-cake and the brandied peaches; for the minister married them in our parlor that afternoon."

One day old Mr. Morgan, the one-armed Civil
War veteran, took me along with him, to get out of
the buckboard and open gates, on the back road
along the river. He was going up to a hill pasture
to salt his sheep. It took forever to get there, because his horse was so slow, and he had time to tell
me a great many stories. This was one of them:
"When I was a boy at school, I worked at Aunt Almera Canfield's doing chores night and morning.
I remember how she used to loosen herself up in the
morning. She was terribly rheumaticky, but she
wouldn't give in to it. Every morning she'd be all
stiffened up so she couldn't stand up straight, nor
hardly move her legs at all; but she'd get herself
dressed somehow, and then two of her sons came in

to help her get started. She'd make them take hold of her, one on each side, and walk her around the room. It was awful to hear how she'd yell out—yell as though they were killing her! And then they'd stop, the sweat on their faces to see how it hurt her, and then she'd yell at them to go on, go on, *she* hadn't asked them to stop! They were over sixty, both of them, with grandchildren themselves, but they didn't dare not do what she said, and they'd walk her round again. She'd kick her poor legs out in front of her hard, to get the joints limbered up, and holler with the pain, and kick them out again, till by and by she'd get so she could go by herself, and she'd be all right for the day. I tell you, I often think of that. Yes, lots of times, it comes back to me."

Up in the sheep pasture, as we sat to rest the horse, he told me this: "I always thought Aunt Almera knew all about the John Brown raid before most folks did—maybe she sent some money to help him. She wasn't a bit surprised, anyhow, when she heard of it, and all through the whole business she never thought of another thing, nor let anybody else. He was caught—any of us that lived in that house those days will never forget a one of those dates— and put in jail on the 9th of October, and his trial

lasted until the 31st. Aunt Almera made us get together in the evenings, me and the hired girl and one
of her grandsons and her daughter, all the family,
and she'd read aloud to us out of the 'Tribune' about
what had happened that day at his trial. I never
saw her so worked up about anything—just like
ashes her old face was, and her voice like cold steel.
We got as excited about it as she did, all of us, especially her grandson, that was about my age. The
day of his execution—December 2d, it was—Aunt
Almera came at dawn to wake me up. 'Put on your
clothes,' says she, 'and go over to the church and
begin to toll the bell.' I didn't need to ask her what
for, either. I'll never forget how awful she looked
to me.

"Well, we tolled the bell all day long, one or the
other of the family, never stopped a minute. You
never heard anything so like death. All day long
that slow, deep clang—and then a stillness—and
then *clang!* again. I could hear it in my head for
days afterwards. Folks came in from all around to
find out what it meant, and Aunt Almera called them
all into her parlor—she sat there all day and never
ate a mouthful of food—and *told* them what it
meant, so they couldn't ever get the sound of her
voice out of their ears. Between times she'd read

out of the Bible to whoever was there, 'Avenge thou
thy cause, O Lord God of battles,' and 'It is time
for thee, O Lord, to lay to thy hand, for they have
destroyed thy law,' and 'Let there be no man to pity
them; nor to have compassion of their fatherless
children.' It was the darndest thing to hear her!

"You'd better believe when Abraham Lincoln sent
out the first call for men there wasn't a boy of military age in our town that didn't enlist!"

An aged cousin had just died, and as we sat
downstairs talking with the doctor, he said to my
aunt, who had been taking care of the sick woman:
"She took it hard!   She took it hard!"

They both frowned, and my aunt looked rather
sick. Then the doctor said, "Not much like your
grandmother, do you remember?"

"Oh, yes, I remember," said my aunt, her face
quivering, her eyes misty, her lips smiling.

The doctor explained to me: "Your great-grandmother was an old, old woman before she ever was
really sick at all, except for rheumatism. And then
she had a stroke of paralysis that left her right side
dead. She lived four days that way—the only days
she'd spent in bed in years, since she was a young

woman, I suppose. Her mind wasn't very clear, she couldn't talk so that we could understand her, and I don't think she rightly knew anybody after her stroke. I guess she went back, 'way back, for we saw from what she did that she thought she had a little baby with her. I suppose she thought she was a young mother again, and that was why she was in bed. We used to see her spread out her arm, very gentle and slow, the only arm she could move, so's to make a hollow place for a little head, and then she'd lie there, so satisfied and peaceful, looking up at the ceiling with a smile in her eyes, as if she felt a little warm, breathing creature there beside her. And sometimes she'd half wake up and stretch out her hand and seem to stroke the baby's head or snuggle it up closer to her, and then she'd give a long sigh of comfort to find it there, and drop off to sleep again, smiling. And she'd always remember, even in her sleep, to keep her arm curved around so there'd be room for the baby; and even in her sleep her face had that shining new-mother look—that old wrinkled face, with that look on it! I've seen lots of death-beds, but I never—" he stopped for a moment.

"Why, at the very last—do you remember?"—he went on to my aunt, "I thought she was asleep, but as I moved a chair she opened her eyes quickly, looked down as if to see whether I had wakened the baby, and looked at me, to warn me to be quiet, her fingers at her lips. 'Sh!' she whispered.

"And that was the way she died."